The Story of God and His People

The House of Israel

Second edition by

Jesslyn De Boer

Beth Lantinga

Rachelle Wiersma

First edition by

Dick J. Ritzema

Wailand Groenendyk

CHRISTIAN SCHOOLS INTERNATIONAL

CHRISTIAN SCHOOLS INTERNATIONAL
3350 East Paris Ave., SE
Grand Rapids, Michigan 49512-3054

Second Edition
© 1998 CHRISTIAN SCHOOLS INTERNATIONAL
Printed in the United States of America
All rights reserved

12 11 10 9 8

ISBN 0-87463-963-8

The development of *The Story of God and His People* was made possible with grants from Christian Schools International Foundation and Canadian Christian Education Foundation, Inc.

Cover photograph by SuperStock.
Biblical quotations are from *The NIV Study Bible*. Copyright 1995 by The Zondervan Corporation. Used with permission.

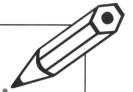

Lookout Point

The sentences below describe some of the people who are part of God's story. See if you can remember who they are. Fill in each blank with one of the names on the list below. Use each name only once.

Abraham	David	Gideon	Joshua	Noah
Adam	Deborah	Isaiah	Moses	Paul
Amos	Eve	Jesus		

1. _____ and _____ sinned by eating the fruit that God had forbidden them to eat.

2. God saved _____ and his family from the flood in the ark.

3. God called _____ and his family to be his special people, and he made a covenant with them.

4. God chose _____ to lead the Israelites out of Egypt.

5. Through God's power _____ and the Israelites conquered Canaan.

6. When the Israelites worshiped idols, God let other nations oppress them. When they repented, God raised up judges such as _____ and _____ to save them.

7. Under King _____ the Israelites became a great nation because he followed God's law.

8. After Israel divided into two nations, prophets such as _____ predicted that Judah and Israel would be captured because of their disobedience to God's law.

9. Throughout the Old Testament times, prophets such as _____ predicted a wonderful time in the future when the messiah would restore peace among nations and bring healing and salvation to all.

10. These promises were partly fulfilled when _____ was born, grew up and ministered to the people, died on the cross, rose again, and ascended to heaven.

11. Jesus' followers, among them Peter and _____, spread the good news about new life in Christ throughout the world.

To see the whole story, fill in the timeline with the names listed on the bottom of this page. Begin with Adam and Eve, and end with your own name. These people—and many more—are part of the one story of God's people, and so are you.

B.C.??	Ancient Times	_____ and _____,
		_____
2200		
2100	Patriarchal Times	_____
2000		
1900		
1800		
1700	Israel in Egypt	
1600		
1500		
1400	Israel in Wilderness	_____
1300		_____
1200	Israel in Canaan	_____, _____
1100		
1000	United Kingdom	_____
900	Divided Kingdom	
800	Prophecies of Fall of	_____, _____
700	Israel and Judah	
600	Exile of Judah	
500	Return of Judah	
400		
300		
200		
100		
A.D.	New Testament Time	_____, _____
100		

1900		
2000		
		_____
		(your name)
???	End of time	

Abraham	David	Gideon	Joshua	Noah
Adam	Deborah	Isaiah	Moses	Paul
Amos	Eve	Jesus		

Name _____

Lookout Point

▲ Looking Back

Age _____

My favorite Bible song was _____

I first knew that Jesus loved me when _____

It made me feel _____

I thought a child of God should act _____

▲ You are Here

Name _____

Date _____

Age _____   Height _____

Personal devotions are easy/hard for me

because _____

I feel the same/different about God as

when I was younger because _____

It's easy/difficult for me to experience

God's love because _____

The most important sign of being a child

of God is _____

▲ In the Future

This year in Bible class I hope to _____

During this year I hope to improve my

relationship with _____

When school is finished I plan to _____

At the end of my story I will be _____

Name _____

The Promise Given

Read the material in the student text and the Bible passages mentioned. Then complete the web.

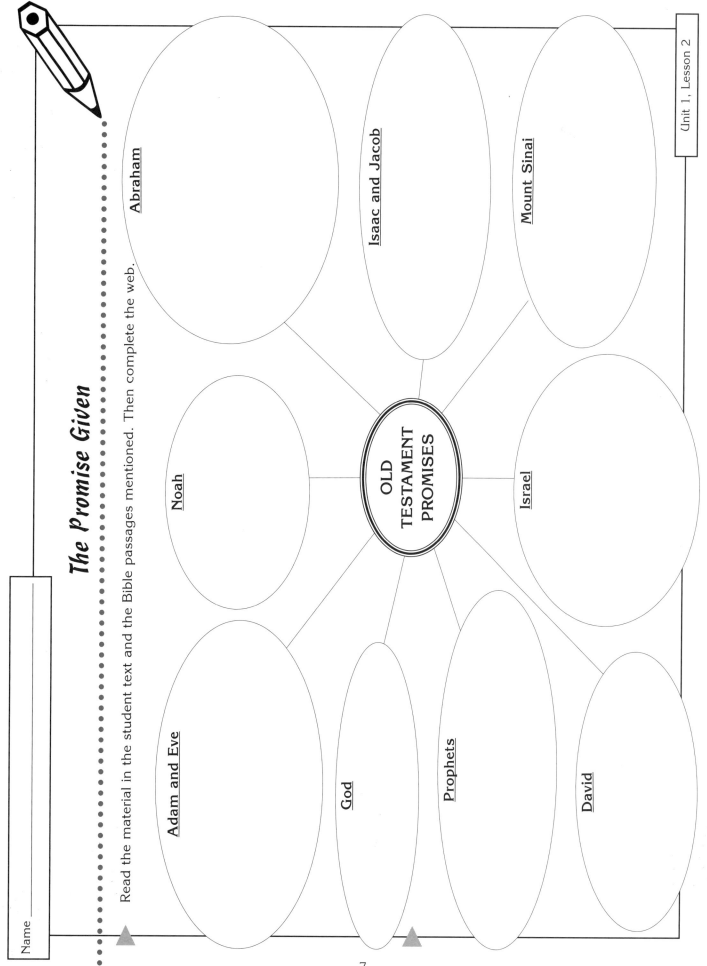

Abraham

Isaac and Jacob

Mount Sinai

Noah

OLD TESTAMENT PROMISES

Israel

Adam and Eve

God

Prophets

David

The Promise Kept

Read the material in your textbook. Then create a cartoon strip or draw symbols for each frame.

The Silent Period	The Silence Is Shattered	The Promise Is Fulfilled	God's Victory
Pentecost	God's Plan for the Church	The Final Victory	God's Plan for Me

God's Faithfulness

To help you discover and compare God's faithfulness in spite of human faithlessness, fill in each blank with the missing word or words. Use your Bible to check your answers.

<u>Human Faithlessness</u>	<u>God's Faithfulness</u>
Adam and Eve disobeyed God.	God gave a _____ (Genesis 3:15).
The world was wicked.	God saved _____ and his family (Genesis 7:1).
Israel murmured in the desert.	God gave _____ and _____ (Exodus 16:12–15).
The people rejected God.	God provided _____ (Judges 2:16).
People were sinful.	God sent _____ (Matthew 1:21).
The people crucified Jesus.	God _____ Jesus from the dead and offered salvation (Acts 2:24).
Saul persecuted the church.	God gave him the _____ (Acts 9:17).

Look back at the completed exercise. What does this tell us about God's relationship with his people? _____

_____

_____

Psalm 136

Look up Psalm 136 in your Bible, and then answer the following questions.

1. Which verses tell how:

    a. God created the earth. _____

    b. God delivered Israel out of Egypt. _____

    c. God led Israel through the desert to the promised land. _____

2. What do verses 1–3 and 26 of this psalm call God's people to do? _____

    _____

3. What refrain is repeated over and over? _____

4. Why do you think those words are repeated after every line? _____

    _____

Name _____

God's Faithfulness

▶1. List as many examples as you can of God's faithfulness for each of the following categories (and any others that you think of).

- God's faithfulness to you personally. _____
  _____
  _____
  _____

- Times when friends or family members have forgiven you. _____
  _____
  _____
  _____

- Signs of God's faithfulness in nature. _____
  _____
  _____
  _____

- Other. _____
  _____
  _____
  _____

▶2. If you want the refrain to be more contemporary, rewrite the words, "His love endures forever."
_____

▶3. Now write your own psalm using the format below:

Two phrases of praise to God based on Psalm 136:1–3.
_____
_____

Refrain _____

Two phrases celebrating God's faithfulness to you.
_____
_____

Refrain _____

Two statements celebrating God's love and faithfulness in the gift of forgiveness.

_____

_____

Refrain _____

Two phrases of praise for God's faithfulness in nature.

_____

_____

Refrain _____

A concluding statement of praise.

_____

_____

Refrain _____

_____

God Speaks

▶ **2 Peter 1:16, 19–21**

1. How can we know that the stories of the Bible were not just made up? _____

_____

2. How does Peter describe the Word of God in verse 19? What is the function of the Word of God?

_____

_____

3. How did the Bible writers get their inspiration? _____

_____

▶ **Genesis 1:1, 26–27, 3:15**

4. Which verse shows God as the Creator? _____

_____

5. Which verse shows God as the Savior? Who will be the winner? _____

_____

_____

6. What model did God use to create humankind? What do you think this means for us? Who

should we model ourselves after? _____

_____

_____

▶ **Deuteronomy 15:7–11 and Matthew 25:34–40**

7. What do these passages have in common? _____

_____

8. What do they say about a life that's pleasing to God? _____

_____

▶ **Deuteronomy 1:17 and James 2:1–4**

9. What do these two passages discuss? _____

_____

_____

_____

Unit 2, Lesson 1

10. Which passage do you think applies more to us? Explain your answer.

_____

_____

_____

_____

_____

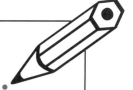

Bible Languages

1. Write this sentence backwards, leaving out all of the vowels.

   _____

2. Open your Bible to Psalm 119. Notice that this psalm is divided into sections, each with a title.

   a. How many sections are there? _____

   b. What do you think the titles are? _____

   c. What are the first and last letters of the Hebrew alphabet? _____

3. Translate this phrase. GGNL WRBH HT (Hint: Think Hebrew!) _____

4. Read each sentence. Decide which language it refers to. Then write **H** (Hebrew), **G** (Greek), or **E** (English) in front of the sentence.

   _____ The Book of Psalms was originally written in this language.

   _____ Paul wrote in this language.

   _____ It has 26 letters in its alphabet.

   _____ Alpha and Omega are the first and last letters in its alphabet.

   _____ It has 24 letters in its alphabet.

   _____ Its alphabet letters go from A to Z.

   _____ The original language of the New Testament.

   _____ It originally was written with no vowels.

   _____ .tfel ot thgir sdaer egaugnal sihT.

   _____ Moses wrote in this language.

   _____ This was the original language of the Old Testament.

5. Why do people translate the Bible into other languages? What is their motivation? See Matthew 28:19–20. _____

   _____

   _____

6. Read Isaiah 49:6 and Genesis 22:18. In what way are Bible translators like Abraham? _____

   _____

   _____

   _____

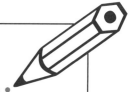

The Library of the Bible

▶ Using the chart in your student text, write the category of each of the following books.

1. Isaiah _____
2. Revelation _____
3. Titus _____
4. 2 Kings _____
5. 3 John _____
6. Judges _____
7. Luke _____
8. Hebrews _____
9. 2 Thessalonians _____
10. Jonah _____

11. Acts _____
12. Exodus _____
13. Deuteronomy _____
14. Micah _____
15. Job _____
16. Lamentations _____
17. Amos _____
18. Ephesians _____
19. Song of Songs _____
20. Mark _____

▶ **Old Testament**   **New Testament**

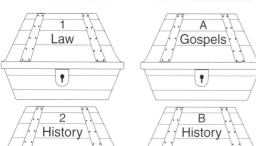

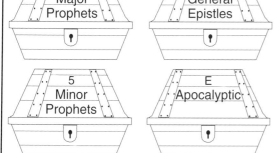

Try to figure out in which treasure chest each of the following treasures could be found.

_____ The story of the Ten Commandments

_____ The story of Pentecost

_____ David's song about the Lord as his shepherd

_____ A description of the new heavens and the new earth

_____ The story about Jesus walking on water

_____ The story of Samson and Delilah

_____ Isaiah's prophecy about the coming messiah

_____ A letter from Paul to Timothy

_____ Jonah's prophecy that Nineveh must repent or be destroyed

_____ John's letter in which he tells his readers to love one another

_____ God's commandments to the Israelites in the desert

The Land of the Bible

Locate and label the following bodies of water: Caspian Sea, Mediterranean (Great) Sea, Persian Gulf, Red Sea, Salt (Dead) Sea, and the Sea of Galilee. Locate and label these rivers: Euphrates, Jordan, Nile, Tigris. Locate and label these cities: Beersheba, Dan, Haran, Jerusalem, Shechem, Ur.

Israel was very small compared with the surrounding nations. Yet it was the birthplace of Christianity, God's greatest gift to the world. Do you think that just one person can make an important difference for good today? How?

God's Timeline

▶Making a Biblical Timeline

1. Cut two sheets of unlined paper in half lengthwise. You should end up with four sheets of paper, each 11" long and 8½" high.

2. Glue or tape the four sheets together. Allow a half-inch overlap on each sheet, so that the four connected sheets measure 42½" in length.

3. On the top write the title God's Story.

4. Starting 2" from the left side of the paper, draw a straight line 38½" inches long down the middle of the sheet.

5. Using your ruler, mark off a ½ vertical line every 1¾". Be sure to make marks at both ends of your long line. You should make a total of 23 vertical lines.

6. Under the first vertical line on the left write "2100 B.C.," under the second, "2000 B.C.," third "1900," fourth "1800," and so on. The second to the last vertical line should have "0" and the final line "A.D. 100."

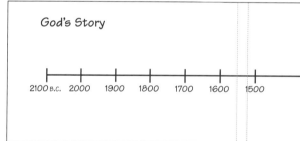

7. Put the events listed below in their correct locations on the timeline. Print the events above the line and the dates underneath.

2066 B.C.	Isaac is born.	586	Babylon captures the southern kingdom.
2006	Jacob and Esau are born.		
1915	Joseph is born.	538	Zerubbabel leads the first return of the exiles.
1898	Joseph is sold.		
1876	Jacob's family moves to Egypt.	515	The temple is rebuilt.
1526	Moses is born.	458	Ezra leads a second return.
1446	Israel leaves Egypt (the exodus).	445	Nehemiah rebuilds Jerusalem's walls.
1406	Moses appoints Joshua leader.		
1220–1050	Period of the judges.	432–5 B.C.	Intertestamentary period.
1105	Samuel is born.	5 B.C.–A.D. 30	Jesus is born, dies, rises from the dead, and ascends to heaven.
1050	Saul becomes king.		
1010	David becomes king.	46–57	Paul makes three missionary journeys.
970	Solomon becomes king.		
933	The kingdom divides.	70	Jerusalem is destroyed.
722	Assyria captures the northern kingdom.	95	John writes the Book of Revelation.

Stories of the Ancient World

	The Story	The Punishment	The Hope
▲ **Adam and Eve** Lessons 1–2			
▲ **Cain, Abel, Seth** Lesson 3			
▲ **Noah** Lessons 4–5			
▲ **The Tower of Babel** Lesson 6			

Unit 3 Organizer

Name _____

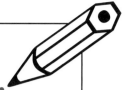

In the Beginning

Use your Bible to fill in the blanks for each phrase from Psalm 105:1–7. Then draw a symbol in each box to help you remember the main idea of each verse.

1. Give _____ to the _____, call on his _____; make known among the _____ what he has _____.	
2. Sing to _____, sing _____ to him; _____ of all his _____ acts.	
3. Glory in his _____ name; let the _____ of those who _____ the _____ rejoice.	
4. _____ to the _____ and his _____; seek his _____ always.	
5. Remember the _____ he has _____, his _____, and the _____ he pronounced,	
6. O _____ of Abraham his _____, O sons of _____, his _____ ones.	
7. He is the _____ our _____; his _____ are in _____ the earth.	

In the Beginning

Reread the myth of Enuma Elish in the student text and complete that part of the chart. Then review the creation story from Genesis 1–2:3 and complete that part of the chart. Then answer the What Do You Think? questions.

	Genesis	Enuma Elish
Who was involved?		
What was it like before the creation of the world?		
How was the earth created?		
How were humans created?		
What were humans meant to be and do?		
Who was to take care of the earth?		

Unit 3, Lesson 1/2

▶What Do You Think?

1. What is the biggest difference between the two stories? _____
   _____
   _____
   _____

2. How do you think the Babylonians came up with the descriptions of their gods? How is the
   Genesis account different? _____
   _____
   _____

3. What does the creation story say about God's relationship with humans? (Hint: look at Genesis
   1:27 and and Genesis 3:8–9.) What was it like before the fall? _____
   _____
   _____

4. Does physical appearance have anything to do with being mirrors of God? _____
   _____

5. What are some characteristics of God that human beings have? _____
   _____
   _____

6. React to this statement: Showing disrespect to another person shows disrespect for God.
   _____
   _____

7. List some things that you have accomplished or difficulties you have overcome that show how
   you mirror God. _____
   _____
   _____
   _____

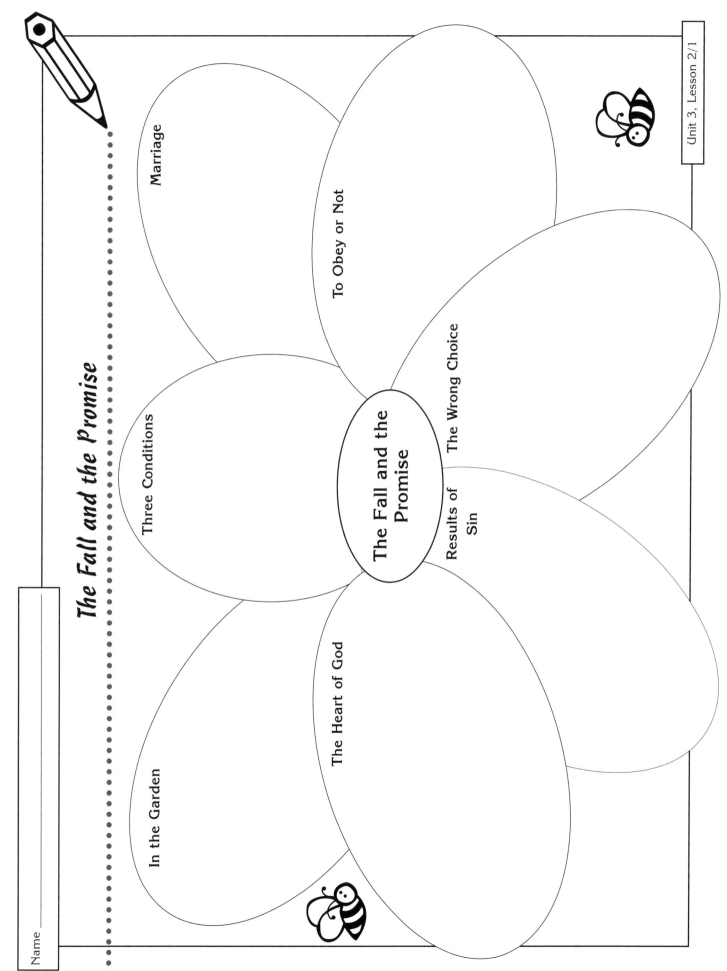

The Fall and the Promise

Name _____

Marriage

To Obey or Not

The Wrong Choice

Three Conditions

The Fall and the Promise

Results of Sin

In the Garden

The Heart of God

The Fall and the Promise

▶ Work through Genesis 2:4–3, using the verse clues to answer the following questions.

1. Describe the Garden of Eden. (Genesis 2:8–10) _____

_____

_____

_____

2. What tasks did God give Adam? (Genesis 2:15, 19–20) _____

_____

3. What relationship did God establish between humankind and nature? (Genesis 2:15 and Genesis

1:28) _____

_____

_____

4. Do you think that we still have that responsibility toward nature today? Explain.

_____

_____

5. What freedom did God want Adam and Eve to enjoy? (Genesis 2:16) _____

_____

_____

6. What was forbidden? Why? (Genesis 2:17) _____

_____

_____

7. Why did God create woman? (Genesis 2:18 and Genesis 1:28) _____

_____

8. Which verses in chapter 3 show the strategies that the serpent used?

   a. He twisted God's intention and encouraged doubt. _____

   b. He appealed to her sense of beauty and delight. _____

9. What did Adam and Eve say to avoid responsibility? (Genesis 3:12–13) _____

_____

10. Why did Adam and Eve hide after they ate the fruit? (Genesis 3:10) _____

_____

11. Complete the following chart to show the results of sin.

	Curse
Satan (3:14–15)	
Eve (3:16)	
Adam (3:17–19)	

12. What did God do to cover Adam and Eve's shame? Genesis 3:21. _____

_____

13. What does this show about God? _____

_____

14. Why didn't God just destroy Adam and Eve? _____

_____

_____

15. How was sending Adam and Eve from the garden a sign of judgment and a sign of mercy?

_____

_____

_____

_____

Cain, Abel, and Seth

▶ Read Genesis 4. Use the class discussion to answer the following questions.

1. Why was God pleased with Abel's offering but not with Cain's? _____
   _____

2. How do we often give our offerings to God? Do you think our offerings are sometimes like Cain's?
   _____
   _____

3. What choice did God give to Cain? (Verse 7.) In what way is Cain's choice our choice?
   _____
   _____

4. What did Cain reveal about his heart when he answered God's question with the question, "Am
   I my brother's keeper?" _____
   _____

5. How did God answer the question? _____
   _____

6. What does the Bible say about Cain's problem in Matthew 5:21–22? Is his problem ever our problem? _____
   _____
   _____

7. What difference might it make if each person in our class consciously tried to be a faithful brother and sister keeper? _____
   _____
   _____

8. What influence did Seth and his descendants have on the world? Read 1 Chronicles 1:1–3 and
   Luke 3:23 and 37. _____
   _____
   _____

God, Noah, and the Flood

Use Genesis 6–8 and **The Gilgamesh Epic** (pages 36–37) to complete the chart.

	Genesis Flood	**The Gilgamesh Epic**
Reason for the flood		
Flood sender		
The condition of God's/gods' heart		
Boat builder		
The boat's cargo		
Where the boat settled		
First action when they left the ark		
God's/god's response		

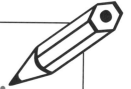

A Fresh Start

▶ A New Beginning (Genesis 9:1–7)

1. What command is common to Genesis 1:28 and Genesis 9:1 and 7? _____
   _____

2. What did God give Noah and his family for food? _____

3. What characteristic did God give animals to protect human life? _____
   _____

4. What command did God give to protect others from the sin of Cain? _____
   _____

5. Why did God give such a severe penalty for murder? _____
   _____

6. How does this section show God's care for humans? _____
   _____

▶ The Covenant Promise (Genesis 9:8–17)

1. What did the covenant promise? _____
   _____

2. What sign did God give? _____

3. How do you know that God made this promise to you? (Hint: see verse 12.) _____
   _____

4. How can you tell that God was making a fresh start with his people? _____
   _____

▶ The Sins of Noah and His Family (Genesis 9:18–29)

1. How did Noah show that sin and foolishness were still in his heart? _____
   _____

2. How did his son Ham show disrespect for his father? _____
   _____

3. How was Ham's family cursed? _____
   _____

4. What does this say about the condition of their hearts? _____

_____

▶What Do You Think?

1. In what ways can this lesson be both serious and comforting? _____

_____

_____

2. What does this lesson say about fresh starts? _____

_____

_____

3. What advice would you give Noah and his sons? _____

_____

_____

_____

Name _____

The Tower of Babel

Read the story of the Tower of Babel in Genesis 11:1–9. Then write a brief summary for each verse in the correct block of the Tower of Babel below.

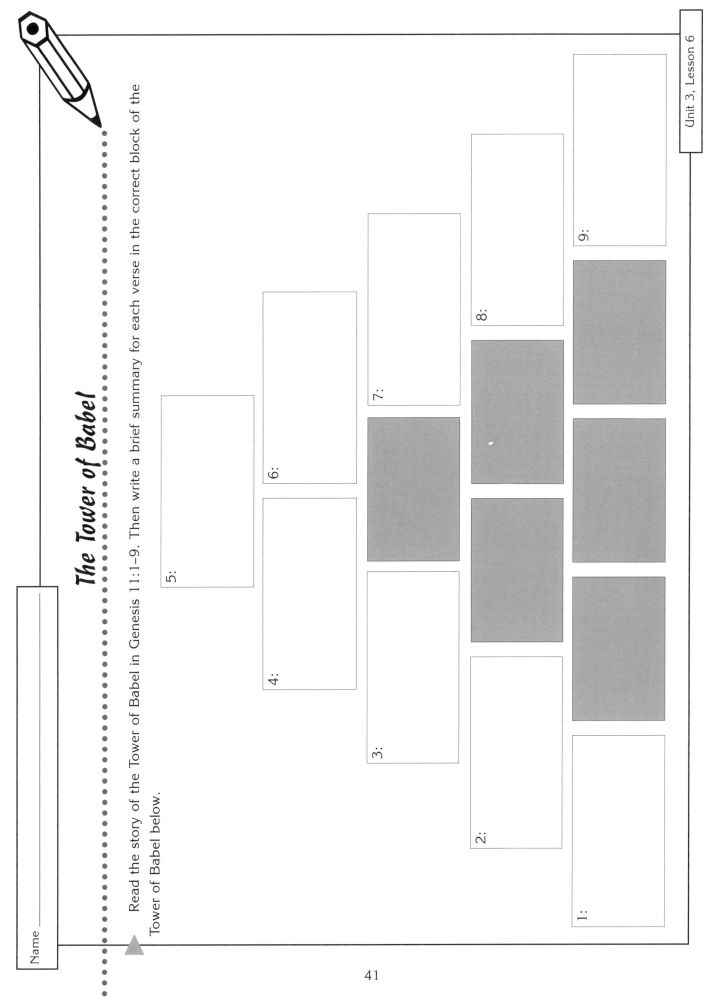

1:

2:

3:

4:

5:

6:

7:

8:

9:

41

▶ 2. React to the following statement:

It's not bad to want to make a name for yourself. _____

_____

_____

_____

▶ 3. Complete the following statement:

Remembering that God gave us our gifts and skills can help us be humble because . . .

_____

_____

_____

The Patriarchs

Lesson	Patriarch/Action	Did It Show Faith?	Consequences
2			
3			
5			
6			
6			

Lesson	Patriarch/Action	Did It Show Faith?	Consequences
7			
7			
8			
9			
12			
14–15			

From Darkness to Light

Read Genesis 11:24—12:5, and then complete the following questions.

1. Whom did Terah take with him out of Ur? _____

2. Where did he intend to go? _____

3. What happened at Haran? _____

4. What did God command Abram to do? (Genesis 12:1)

   "Leave your _____, your _____, and your

   _____."

5. What promises did God guarantee to Abram if he obeyed God? (Genesis 12:2–3)

   "I will make you into a great _____

   and I will _____ _____ you;

   I will make your _____ great,

   and you will be a _____.

   I will _____ those who _____ you,

   and whoever _____ you I will _____;

   and all _____ on earth

   will be blessed through _____."

6. What was Abram's response to God's call? _____

7. What is spiritual darkness? _____

   _____

8. What kinds of gods do people worship today? _____

   _____

   _____

Abram's Failure and God's Faithfulness

▶ Read the story of Abram in Egypt from Genesis 12:10–20. Then read the following statements and write a brief explanation about the situation. List the verse or verses where it can be found.

1. Abram was in a difficult and dangerous situation. _____
_____

2. Abram lied to save his own life. _____
_____

3. Abram put his marriage in danger. _____
_____
_____

4. Pharaoh acted like a powerful pagan ruler. _____
_____
_____

5. God sent a message to Pharaoh. _____
_____

6. God rescued Abram. _____
_____

▶**What Do You Think?**

7. What message did God want Abram to hear? _____
_____

8. Abram didn't trust God. Yet God protected and blessed him. Why? _____
_____

9. Read 1 Peter 5:6–7. What advice might Peter have given to Abram? _____
_____
_____

10. How does the following paraphrase of Psalm 32:2 fit this story of Abram? "Fortunate the person against whom the Lord does not keep score." What does it say to us? _____
_____
_____

A Light in Darkness

Read the appropriate verses for each section. Then complete the related activities.

▶ **Lot Chooses—Genesis 13**

1. Verses 5–7. What might the shepherds of Lot and Abram have said to each other?

   Abram's shepherd "_____"

   Lot's shepherd   "_____"

2. Verses 8–9. How might Abram have said this today? _____
   _____

3. Verse 10. What was Lot's land like? _____

4. Verses 12–13. Finish writing this note that Abram might have sent to Lot.

   Dear Lot,

        I know that the land near Sodom is beautiful, but I want you to know that

   I'm worried about you because . . .

   _____

   _____

   _____

   _____

   Sincerely,
Uncle Abram

5. Verses 14–17. What do these signs stand for? _____
   _____

   _____

6. Verse 18. Make a small drawing that shows how Abram was faithful to God.

Lot Gets Kidnapped—Genesis 14:8–16

1. Verses 8–12. Complete the following script for a news flash that interrupts your favorite television show.

> Our news team in the Middle East has just reported that Babylonian invaders have defeated our armies. Some of our men escaped into the hills. _____

_____

_____

_____

_____

2. Verses 13. What did the breathless survivor say to Abram? _____

_____

_____

_____

3. Verses 14–16. What did Abram recover for Lot? _____

_____

Abraham Meets the Kings—Genesis 14:17–24.

Two kings—the king of Sodom and Melchizedek—came out to meet Abram. You can learn a lot about Abram from what they say. Identify the king who might have made each of the following statements.

1. I was eager to make friends with Abram. Anyone who defeated the Babylonians could make mincemeat out of me! _____

2. I came to serve Abram. Obviously God Most High had blessed him. _____

3. God gave Abram the victory over his enemies. _____

4. I told Abram I'd give him of all the loot, but he said no. _____

5. Abram gave me a tenth of everything that he had gained. _____

6. Abram told me that he had promised the Lord not to accept anything from me. _____

_____

7. Abram told me to share the loot with the other fighting men. _____

8. Abram did what was faithful and right. _____

9. Abram was foolish! _____

Name _____

A Smoking Fire Pot with a Blazing Torch

1. Read Genesis 15. How did God greet Abram in the vision? _____

   _____

2. What protest did Abram make to God? _____

3. It was common in Abram's time for a man without children to adopt a servant to be his heir.

   What servant was Abram planning to make his heir? _____

4. How did God reassure Abram? _____

   _____

5. Reread the description of the ceremony in Genesis 15:9–11, 17. What did God tell Abram to do?

   _____

   _____

6. List four things that God told Abram about his descendants.

   • _____

   • _____

   • _____

   • _____

7. Answer the questions below about the royal grant God made to Abram in Genesis 15.

   a. Who is the king? _____

   b. Who is the servant? _____

   c. What benefit does he receive? _____

   d. What is his faithful service? _____

   e. What symbolizes of the oath? _____

   f. Why didn't God get angry with Abram's questions? _____

   _____

   _____

The Sign of Circumcision

▶ Read **Understanding Ancient Customs** (page 48) in your text. Then answer these questions.

1. What action showed that Abram and Sarai did not fully trust God's promises? _____
   _____

2. What resulted when they took matters into their own hands? _____
   _____

3. How did God reveal his concern for people outside the covenant? _____
   _____

▶ Read Genesis 17. Then answer the following questions.

1. What action showed Abram's fear and reverence for God? _____
   _____

2. Complete the suzerain-vassal chart below.

Suzerain's (God's) Promises	Vassal's (Abraham's) Requirements
a. _____ _____	a. _____ _____
b. _____ _____	b. _____ _____
c. _____ _____	c. _____ _____
d. _____ _____	

3. What did God promise Sarah? _____

4. What was Abraham's first response to God's promise of a son? _____
   _____

5. Which son would carry on the covenant with God? _____

6. What did God promise to Ishmael? _____
   _____

7. What sign marks us today as God's children? _____

Good News and Bad News

Read the assigned verses from Genesis 19. Then tell how you know the following.

	Verses	Actions
1. Lot knew how to extend hospitality to strangers.	1–3	
2. Lot recognized his obligation to protect his visitors.	6–8	
3. The Lord was determined to preserve Lot and his family.	10–12, 16, 21–22	
4. Lot may have found it difficult to trust his angelic visitors.	16	
5. Lot's wife found it impossible to leave the city of Sodom.	26	
6. God honored Abraham's request.	29	

The Son of the Promise

Use Genesis 21:1–20 for reference if necessary. Place each of the following statements under "Anguish" or "Joy."

His life was a miracle.

Both would be great nations.

God kept his promise to Sarah.

His birth brought happy laughter to Sarah.

His name was Isaac, meaning "laughter."

His name was Ishmael, meaning "God heard."

It pained Abraham to send him away.

He was not the son of the promise.

Hagar's water was gone.

God cared for Hagar and Ishmael.

He would carry on God's promise of blessing.

His birth resulted from Abraham and Sarah's doubt.

Anguish									Joy								

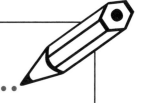

Love and Death

1. When Abraham was old, he said to his chief servant, "Swear by the Lord . . . that you will not get a wife for my son from the daughters of the _____ . . . but will go to my country and my own relatives and get a wife for my son Isaac." (Genesis 24:1–6)

   Abraham expressed his faith in the Lord when he told his servant that God would send his _____ to help in this mission. If the woman refused to come back with the servant, Abraham's servant was _____ from his oath. (Genesis 24:7–9)

   The servant took ten _____ and all kinds of other good things along with him when he left. He arrived at his destination toward evening. He prayed that God would give him _____. He asked God for _____ to lead him to the right girl: the girl to be Isaac's wife would offer to give him and his camels _____. (Genesis 24:10–14)

2. He had not even finished praying when _____ the daughter of Bethuel, Milcah's son, approached. She was a beautiful young woman. And she offered him a _____ and drew water for his camels. When the camels had finished drinking, Abraham's servant took out a _____ and two _____. (Genesis 24:15–22)

   Rebekah then introduced herself and invited the servant to stay at her home. They had plenty of _____ and _____ for the animals, she told him. Then the servant bowed down and worshiped the _____. He praised God for leading him to the house of _____ relatives. (Genesis 24:23–28)

3. Rebekah's brother, _____, went to greet Abraham's servant. The animals were unloaded and cared for. Water was brought so Abraham's men could _____. Food was set before Abraham's servant, but he _____ until he first explained _____ . (Genesis 24:29–33)

   Abraham's servant told the whole story of his mission and how _____ had led him to _____. Then both _____ and his father Bethuel said, "This is from the _____; we can say nothing to you one way or the other. Here is

_____ ; take her and go, and let her become the _____ of your master's son, as the _____ has directed." (Genesis 24:34–51)

4. The servant _____ to the ground before the Lord. He presented the _____ to Rebekah and also gave costly gifts to her _____ and to her _____. This was the custom, which showed that Rebekah was very valuable to the entire family. (Genesis 24:52–54)

The next morning Abraham's _____ was ready to go, but Rebekah's brother and mother requested that she remain _____ days before she left with him for Hebron. But the servant was eager to be on his way. When they asked Rebekah, she said, "_____." (Genesis 24:54–58)

5. So they sent Rebekah on her way, along with her _____, and blessed her saying, "Our sister, may you increase to _____." So Abraham's servant, his men, Rebekah, and her maids left. (Genesis 24:59–61)

Now _____ was in the _____ one evening, and when he looked up, he saw _____ approaching. Rebekah also looked up and saw him. She asked, "Who is that man in the field coming to meet us?" When the servant said it was _____, his master, she took her _____ and covered herself. Then the servant told Isaac all he had done. Isaac brought Rebekah into _____ tent and _____ her. Rebekah _____ Isaac after Sarah's death, and he _____ her. (Genesis 24:62–66)

Name _____

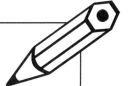

A Bitter Conflict and a Blessing

Review Genesis 25:19–34 and 27:1–30, looking for actions of Jacob and Esau that reveal their character. Record at least three actions for each of them in the first column. In the second column, write the character trait that each action reveals.

	What He Did	Character Quality
Jacob		
Esau		

Answer the following questions.

1. Which of the two brothers was considered unworthy in the eyes of of their world?

    _____

2. Based on your observations of Jacob and Esau, which one deserved the covenant blessing?

    _____

    _____

    _____

3. What does it show about God that he chose Jacob? _____

    _____

    _____

    _____

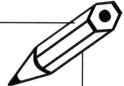

Angels on a Ziggurat

▶**Genesis 28:10–22**

1. Complete the following sentences that tell about God's promises.

    a. I am the _____

    b. I will give your and _____

    c. Your descendants will be _____

    _____

    d. All peoples on earth will be _____

    e. I am with _____

    _____

    f. I will not _____

2. Of what earlier promise do God's words to Jacob remind you? _____

    _____

3. What New Testament promise does Genesis 28:15 point to? (See Matthew 28:20.)

    _____

4. What two-part vow did Jacob make? _____

    _____

5. How did his meeting with God affect Jacob? _____

    _____

▶**Genesis 29:14b–30**

1. How was Jacob deceived? _____

    _____

2. Why do you think Jacob wanted to marry Rachel? _____

    _____

3. What arrangement did Laban and Jacob make? _____

    _____

4. What do you think would happen in Jacob's marriages? Why? _____

    _____

Unit 4, Lesson 10

Name _____

Jacob's Baby Boom

Use Genesis 29:31—30:24 to complete the crossword puzzle.

Across

4. Leah's youngest child and only daughter.
6. Jacob's only son not mentioned in Genesis 30.
8. The second son born to Bilhah.
9. His mother hoped that Jacob would love her because this new baby was the third son.
11. His name means "happy."
13. "I will praise the Lord." Jacob's fourth son.

Down

1. The son of good fortune.
2. He was a precious gift from God.
3. Jacob's fifth son, the brother of Naphtali.
5. His mother said, "God has rewarded me."
7. His birth removed his mother's disgrace.
10. His name means "the Lord has heard."
12. Leah's firstborn son.

List the names of Jacob's children under their mothers' names. Behind the name indicate the order in which they were born.

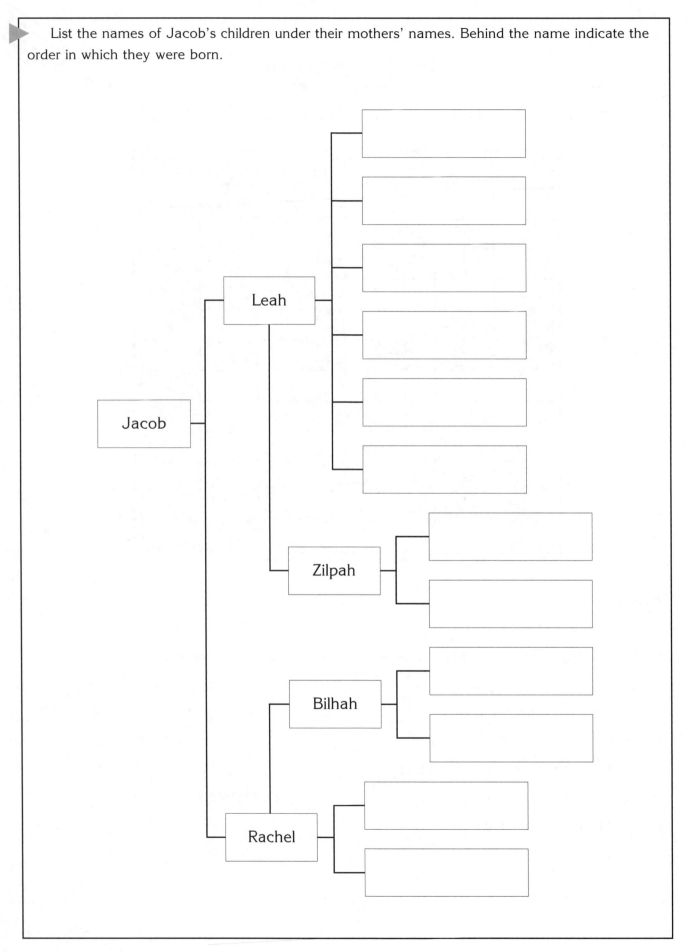

Jacob Goes Home

Read Genesis 31:22–55, and then complete the outline.

1. Laban pursues Jacob.

    a. Laban pursues Jacob and catches up with him.

    b. God _____

2. Laban confronts Jacob.

    a. Laban tells Jacob that he shouldn't have gone without saying goodbye.

    b. Laban tells about his plans for _____

    c. Laban accuses Jacob of _____

3. Jacob defends himself.

    a. Jacob lets Laban _____

    b. Rachel is _____

    c. Jacob angrily accuses Laban of _____

4. Jacob and Laban make a covenant.

    a. They set up some _____

    b. They agree not to _____

    c. They take an _____ to swear that they will abide by the covenant.

    d. Jacob offers a _____

    e. They share a _____

Unit 4, Lesson 12

Dreamer Drama

Read Genesis 37. Then match the name with its correct description.

_____ 1. We bought Joseph.   a. Israel

_____ 2. I was the oldest of Jacob's sons; I tried to protect Joseph.   b. Joseph

_____ 3. Joseph was put in a pit at this place.   c. Egypt

_____ 4. We sold Joseph for twenty shekels of silver.   d. Dothan

_____ 5. I was the captain of Pharaoh's guard.   e. Reuben

_____ 6. Joseph was sold a second time in this country.   f. Potiphar

_____ 7. I was called "the dreamer."   g. brothers

_____ 8. Jacob's descendants became a nation called by this name.   h. Midianites

Answer the following questions.

1. Why did Joseph's brothers hate him so much? _____

_____

_____

2. How would his brothers have acted if they had better understood Joseph's dreams?

_____

_____

3. Would Joseph have acted differently if he had understood his dreams? _____

_____

_____

4. What hint of hope does the story hold? _____

_____

5. How can you tell that God was active in this story? _____

_____

6. What did Joseph's dreams point to? _____

_____

_____

Unit 4, Lesson 13

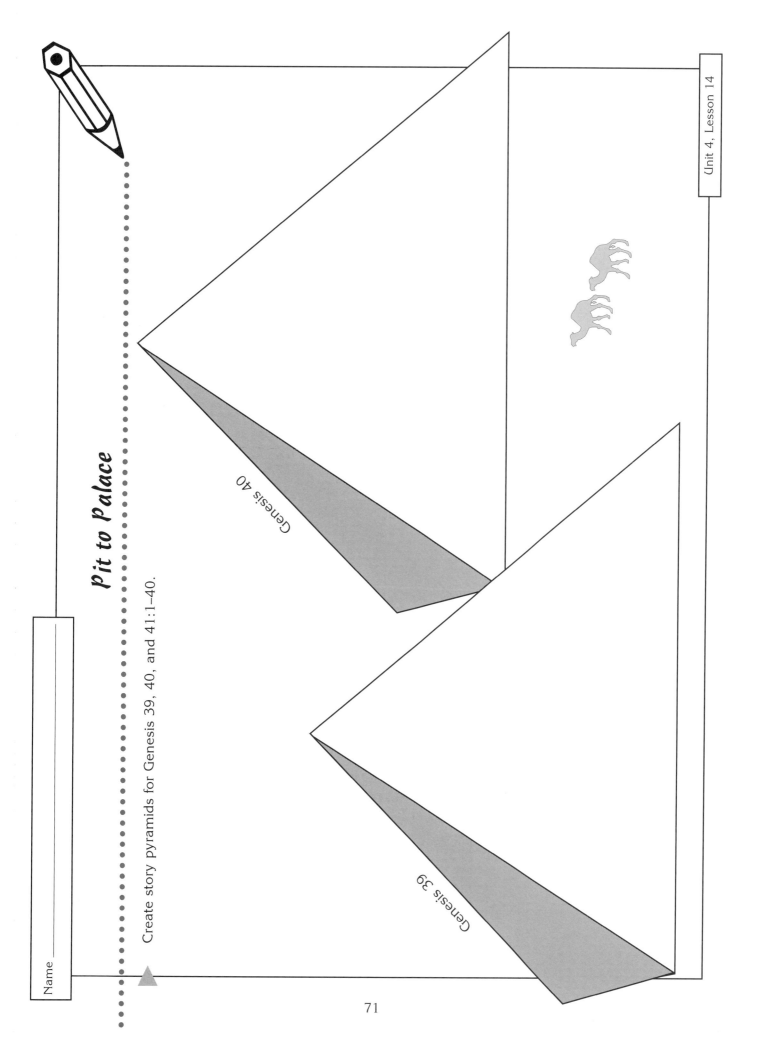

Name

Pit to Palace

Create story pyramids for Genesis 39, 40, and 41:1–40.

Genesis 40

Genesis 39

Genesis 41:1-40

Reunion

Use Genesis 42–45 to help you answer the following questions.

1. Why didn't Joseph's brothers recognize him? _____
   _____

2. What did the brothers expect from God? What do we most fear when we are guilty of something?
   _____
   _____
   _____

3. How did Joseph's actions probably appear to his brothers at first? Did Joseph have a reason to
   appear harsh? _____
   _____
   _____

4. Why do you think that Joseph didn't tell them who he was? _____
   _____

5. How was Joseph's dream fulfilled? See Genesis 42:6–8. _____
   _____

6. Had the brothers forgotten what they had done to Joseph? How can you tell? See Genesis
   42:21–22. _____
   _____

7. What made Joseph cry in Genesis 42:24? What does this say about Joseph? _____
   _____
   _____

8. What does 43:29–30 reveal about Joseph? _____
   _____

9. How can you tell that the brothers were no longer cold and hardhearted? _____
   _____
   _____
   _____

Unit 4, Lesson 15

10. What aspect of God's character did Joseph reveal to his brothers? _____

_____

_____

_____

11. Why was Jacob able to send his beloved son Benjamin to Egypt? (See Genesis 43:14.)

_____

12. Who in this story showed understanding of God's care and his guiding hand in human events?

How? _____

_____

13. Why might Genesis 50:19–21 be a good summary of this lesson? _____

_____

_____

_____

_____

_____

Name _____

From Slavery to a Covenant

Lesson Summary	What It Says about God	What It Says to Me
1.		
2.		
3.		
4.		
5.		
6.		

Lesson Summary	What It Says about God	What It Says to Me
7.		
8.		
9.		
10.		
11.		
12.		
13.		

Lesson Summary	What It Says about God	What It Says to Me
14.		
15.		
16.		
17.		

A New King in Egypt

▶Exodus 1

1. Why was Pharaoh afraid of the Israelites? _____
   _____

2. In what two ways did Pharaoh try to control the Israelites? _____
   _____

3. Why didn't Shiphrah and Puah obey Pharaoh? _____

4. Why do you think only the baby boys were to be killed? _____
   _____

5. Do you think there are times today when a person should disobey authorities? _____
   _____
   _____

▶Exodus 2:1–10 and Hebrews 11:23

1. Why did Moses' parents hide him for three months? (Hebrews 11:23) _____
   _____

2. Why did God spare Moses' life? _____

3. What might God be sparing and preparing you for? How do we discover God's plan for our own
   lives? _____
   _____

4. How do you suppose Miriam felt when Pharaoh's daughter and her attendants found Moses?
   _____
   _____

5. How do you think Moses' mother felt when the princess gave Moses back to her for a little while?
   How did she feel when she had to give Moses back to the princess? _____
   _____
   _____

▶Consider the Story

1. The powerful Pharaoh had ordered all Israelite baby boys killed. But Moses was saved by women
   who dared to disobey Pharaoh. List the women and explain what they did. _____
   _____
   _____

2. *Providence* is a word that describes how God provides for his children. How do you see God's providence in Moses' life? _____

_____

3. Describe a time in your life when God protected and provided for you. _____

_____

_____

_____

4. Try to remember and describe a time when you or someone you know did something good that required special courage from God. _____

_____

_____

_____

5. What kinds of slavery do people encounter today? _____

_____

_____

Gods, Gods, and More Gods

1. Why do you think Moses killed the Egyptian? _____
_____

2. Why do you think the fighting Hebrew resented Moses? _____
_____
_____
_____

3. Whom did Moses choose to identify with? _____
_____
_____

4. Was Moses ready to be a leader? Why? _____
_____
_____

5. Who chooses to identify with the poor and oppressed today? _____
_____
_____

6. How did God use Moses' wilderness experience? _____
_____
_____
_____

7. Do you think it was easy for Moses to reject all the advantages of his Egyptian upbringing? Why?
_____
_____
_____

8. How did Moses' act of murder change his life? _____
_____
_____

Read Hebrews 11:24–26 and **Egyptian Religion** and **Hebrew Religion** (pages 73–74) in your text. Then complete the chart that shows what Moses rejected and what he affirmed.

Moses Rejected	Moses Accepted
Polytheism—	Monotheism—
Sun god—	Theocracy—
Man with crocodile head—	
Man with falcon's head—	
Man with ram's head—	
Woman with lioness's head—	
Egyptian gods of—	

Name _____

Moses, Are You Listening?

Read Exodus 3, and then fill in the blanks with the correct words from the Bible passage.

Moses was tending _____ sheep, and he came to Mount _____, the mountain of God. An angel of the Lord appeared to Moses in a _____ that did not _____ up.

When Moses approached the bush to see this strange sight, _____ said, "Do not _____. Take off your _____, for the place where you are standing is _____ ground." Then he said, "I am the God of your _____, the God of _____, the God of _____, and the God of _____." At this, Moses hid his face, because he was afraid to look at _____.

God told Moses that he had seen the misery of his people in _____ and that he had come down to _____ them—to bring them into the land flowing with _____ and _____, the home of the _____ and other tribes.

Moses felt unworthy to bring the people out of Egypt. He said to God, "Who am I, that I should go to _____ and bring the _____ out of _____." But God assured Moses that he would be with him, and he gave Moses a _____: Israel would return to worship God on that _____ after their release from Egypt.

Moses then asked how he should introduce the God who had sent him.

God said, "'_____. This is what you are to say to the Israelites: '_____' has sent me to you.'" God also told Moses that God's name would last _____, and he would be remembered from _____ to _____.

God instructed Moses to go to the _____ of Israel and tell them to take a _____ journey into the desert to _____ to the Lord. Moses was to ask Pharaoh's permission to go. God told Moses that Pharaoh would not let them go until God stretched out his _____ to strike the Egyptians with all the _____ he could perform. And Israel would not leave Egypt _____-handed. God promised that the Egyptians would give the Israelites articles of _____ and _____ and clothing.

► Read Exodus 3:11–4:17 to find Moses' reasons for not serving God. Then find God's answers to Moses.

Moses' Concerns	God's Answers
3:11	
3:13	
4:1	
4:10	
4:13	

► Use words or drawings to describe the three signs God gave Moses to convince the people of Israel that he was real.

Name _____

Let My People Go

As you read the stories of the plagues look for and record the following items. If they do not occur in a particular plague story, leave the box empty.

Plague	Warning	Pharaoh	Magicians/Officials	Israelites
1. Water to blood. Exodus 7: 14–24:				
2. Frogs. Exodus 8: 1–15				
3. Gnats. Exodus 8: 16–19				
4. Flies. Exodus 8: 20–32				

Plague	Warning	Pharaoh	Magicians/Officials	Israelites
5. Plague on livestock. Exodus 9: 1-7				
6. Boils. Exodus 9: 8-12				
7. Hail. Exodus 9: 13-35				
8. Locusts. Exodus 10: 1-20				
9. Darkness. Exodus 10: 21-29				

The Blood of the Lamb

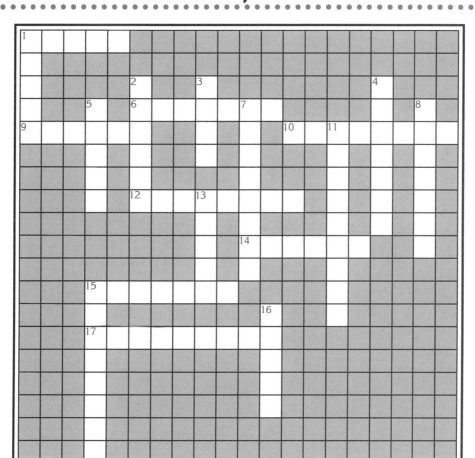

▶ACROSS

1. The lamb's _____ could not be broken (verse 46).
6. This is how the people ate the Passover meal (two words, verse 11).
9. The lamb had be without _____ (verse 5).
10. The firstborn died at this hour.
12. Lamb was cooked by _____ it over the fire (verse 9).
14. This plant was used to put the blood of the lamb on the doorframes (verse 21).
15. The gold, silver, and other resources the Israelites took from Egypt was called _____ (verse 36).
17. The ceremony was the passover _____ to the Lord (verse 27).

▶DOWN

1. The people were told to put _____ on their doorframes (verse 7).
2. The people ate these kind of herbs (verse 8).
3. A _____ was killed to spare Israel's firstborn sons (verse 3).
4. The loud _____ of the Egyptians could be heard when they discovered their sons had died (verse 30).
5. The bread couldn't include this time-consuming ingredient (verse 8).
7. The lamb was to be killed at this time (verse 6).
8. Even this ruler's son was killed (verse 29).
11. The blood kept him out of the houses in Goshen (verse 23).
13. If a family was too small to eat a whole lamb, they had to _____ with their neighbor (verse 4).
15. This event foreshadowed Jesus' death.
16. Our substitute for the lamb is _____.

Don't Be Afraid

Read Exodus 13:17—14:31. Then find the verses that describe each of the key events below.

1. God, Yahweh, was present among his people. He led them with a pillar of cloud in the daytime and a pillar of fire at night.   _____

2. God showed his power to gain glory and to show the Egyptians that he is the Lord.   _____

3. The Israelites complained and quarreled with Moses when the Egyptians threatened them at the sea.   _____

4. Moses told the people to not be afraid and to stand firm because God was going to deliver them.   _____

5. The angel of God and the pillar of cloud moved between the Israelites and the Egyptians. During the night it brought light to the Israelites and darkness to the Egyptians, and it protected God's people.   _____

6. When Moses stretched out his hand, God sent a strong east wind that divided the waters of the sea. The wind also dried a pathway between the walls of water so that the Israelites could pass through on dry ground.   _____

7. When Moses stretched out his hand again, God released the walls of water. Pharaoh and all the Egyptians were swept into the sea, and not one survived.   _____

8. When the Israelites saw what had happened to the Egyptians, they feared the Lord and began to trust God and Moses.   _____

Answer the following questions.

1. In what ways are you like the Israelites? _____

    _____

    _____

2. Have you ever felt scared, trapped, and afraid to go on? How did you get through the experience? How did you decide what to do? Did you experience God's presence during the event?

_____

_____

_____

_____

3. Do you know anyone who has escaped a form of slavery? How did they achieve their freedom?

_____

_____

_____

_____

▶ Illustrate the story events.

1. Fold your strip of paper into five 4½" sections. You should have a long strip of paper with four folds and five sections.

2. Choose five of the key events from the first section of this activity. Then illustrate each one on a section. Be sure to illustrate them in order.

3. When you finish illustrating the Israelites' story events, think about your own story and your answers to the questions in the second section. Turn your story strip over. On one or more of the sections there, illustrate an event from your life or from the life of someone you know.

The Horse and Its Rider

▶ Identify the kind of parallelism used in the following verses of Exodus 15: similar, contrasting, or completing.

1. verse 1 _____
2. verse 4 _____
3. verse 6 _____
4. verses 9–10 _____
5. verse 11 _____

6. verse 13 _____
7. verse 14 _____
8. verse 15 _____
9. verse 17 _____

▶ Three of the five stanzas in Moses and Miriam's song end with similes. Can you find them? Write them, including the verse reference.

a. _____

b. _____

c. _____

▶ The song gives a picture of God and describes his actions.

a. How does the song picture God? _____

b. Which verses of the song describe what God had already done? _____

c. Which verses of the song describe what God was going to do? _____

▶ Write a poem of praise for God's goodness in your life. Be sure to include two kinds of parallelism and at least one simile. Make your poem at least six lines long.

_____

_____

_____

_____

_____

_____

_____

_____

_____

_____

_____

Name _____

Grace for Grumblers

As you read the story of Israel's wanderings in Exodus 15:22—16:30 and 17:1–7, draw a dotted line from the name of each place to its location on the map and then a solid line that connects the stops on their route. Complete the questions in each box.

Desert of Shur
What led to the Israelites' grumbling?

Desert of Sin
What did God want them

to follow?

to know?

to see?

to gather?

to rest from?

to trust?

Rephidim
What does the gift of water show about God?

Marah
Whom were the people really quarreling with?

How was Moses a peace-maker and mediator?

How did God remind the people of his covenant promises?

Elim
What marvelous blessing did God provide here? What does it say about God?

EGYPT

GOSHEN

Great Sea

CANAAN

EDOM MOAB

MIDIAN

SINAI DESERT

Mount Sinai

Red Sea

North

0   40   80 100 mi.

0   40   80   120 km.

Name _____

Sinai Shakes

▶ After you read Exodus 19, find the verses that show the following.

1. God delivered his people from slavery in Egypt and carried them on eagles' wings.   _____

2. God renewed the covenant with his people. He revealed that true blessing comes only through obedience to God.   _____

3. The people responded positively when the covenant was explained.   _____

4. God's voice would cause the people to put their trust in him.   _____

5. Preparation for meeting with God included cleansing, obedience, and recognizing God's holiness.   _____

6. God revealed his majesty and awesome power with the blast of trumpets, fire, smoke, thunder and lightning.   _____

7. Through Moses God warned the people to respect the holiness God's presence brought to the mountain.   _____

▶ As you consider this story, ask yourself these questions.

1. Where and when do you see God's majesty?

_____

_____

2. Respond to the following statement. "Holiness isn't as important today as it was at Mount Sinai." Tell whether you agree or not, and explain your reasons.

_____

_____

_____

3. For the Israelites, the physical act of cleansing themselves in preparation for meeting with God was important because it symbolized the preparation of their hearts. How do you prepare for worship? Is it as important to prepare our hearts today as it was at Mount Sinai?

_____

_____

_____

4. What does it mean to you to be consecrated to God?

_____

_____

_____

_____

Near Eastern Covenants

Use your text and the Bible references. In the first column, explain Hittite suzerain-vassal covenants. In the second column, describe the Sinai covenant.

	Hittite Covenants	Sinai Covenant
Preamble (Exodus 20:1)		
Prologue (Exodus 20:2)		
Stipulations (Exodus 20:3–17)		
Witnesses (Exodus 24:9–10)		
Curses and Blessings		

Unit 5, Lesson 10

1. How did the Israelites respond to the covenant? (See Exodus 24:3, 7.) Do you think that they would always keep their word? Why? _____

_____

_____

2. What promise did God make to the people? (See Exodus 23:20–22.) _____

_____

3. Will God always keep his word? _____

4. Do you think that God cares as much about you as he cared for the mixed up Israelites at Mount Sinai? Why? _____

_____

5. "Rules won't take us to heaven, but they do help us live more happily while we are here on earth." What do you think this statement means? _____

_____

_____

The Ten Commandments and You

▶ Write the commandments on the correct tablet.

Vertical Commandments

_____

_____

_____

_____

Horizontal Commandments

_____

_____

_____

_____

_____

_____

▶ New Testament references that explain the commandments are listed here. Match each reference with its summary.

_____ 1. Speak the truth in love.

_____ 2. Work so you can share with those in need.

_____ 3. Husbands, love your wives; wives, respect your husbands.

_____ 4. The Sabbath was made for humans, but Jesus is Lord of it.

_____ 5. Be content with what you have.

_____ 6. God is Spirit, so worship him in spirit and truth.

_____ 7. Submit to those in authority.

_____ 8. Don't swear by anything in heaven or on earth.

_____ 9. Don't be angry or speak in anger.

_____ 10. Love God with your heart, soul and mind.

a. Ephesians 5:33

b. Hebrews 13:5

c. Ephesians 4:15

d. Matthew 22:37

e. Romans 13:1

f. Matthew 5:22

g. Mark 2:27–28

h James 5:12

i. John 4:24

j. Ephesians 4:28

Below are the Ten Commandments. Match each New Testament reference from the previous section with its corresponding commandment and write the number on the line.

Have no other gods.　　　　_____

Make no images.　　　　_____

Keep God's name holy.　　　　_____

Keep God's day holy.　　　　_____

Honor your parents.　　　　_____

Don't murder.　　　　_____

Don't commit adultery.　　　　_____

Don't steal.　　　　_____

Don't lie.　　　　_____

Don't covet anything.　　　　_____

Name _____

Holy, Holy, Holy

▶ Answer the following questions using Exodus 28–29.

1. Who was Israel's first high priest? _____

2. How did people get to be priests? _____

3. Why did God have the priests wear special garments? _____
_____

4 Why were the names of the twelve tribes engraved on the stones for the ephod's shoulder pieces?
_____
_____

5. What was the main work of the priests? (See Leviticus 1:5–9.) _____
_____

6. What two items did the high priest use to know the will of God? (See Exodus 28:30.) _____
_____

7. How did Jesus become the perfect High Priest? (See Hebrews 7:27.) _____
_____

8. How does he still act as our High Priest? (See Romans 8:26–27.) _____
_____

9. Look at the following passages to see how you can serve as a priest today.

   a. Romans 12:1 _____

   b. Matthew 5:44 _____

   c. Matthew 18:21–22 _____

10. How do we know God's will for our lives? _____
_____
_____

11. What do you think it means to be a living sacrifice? In what situations will you make a sacrifice
to be known as a child of God? _____
_____
_____
_____

The Scapegoat

Five types of sacrifices are listed below. Read the Bible references for a description of each sacrifice. Then match the name to its correct description, writing the correct letter in each blank.

_____ Grain offering—Leviticus 2:1–2

_____ Burnt offering—Leviticus 1:3, 10, 14

_____ Fellowship offering—Leviticus 3:1; 7:11–13

_____ Sin offering—Leviticus 4:3, 13–14, 22–23; 5:7, 11

_____ Guilt offering—Leviticus 5:14–16

a. A bull, ram, or male bird with no defects was offered voluntarily for unintentional sin or as an expression of love for the Lord.

b. Fine flour, olive oil, and incense were offered voluntarily to thank God for his goodness.

c. Bread or a perfect animal from a flock or herd was offered as an act of thanksgiving and peace with God.

d. A perfect ram of the proper value was required as payment for unintentional sin; a 20 percent fine was also paid.

e. A young bull for the high priest and people, a male goat for the leader, a dove or pigeon for the poor, or a small amount of flour from the very poor was required for unintentional sins, confession and forgiveness of sin, or cleansing from defilement.

Read about the Day of Atonement in Leviticus 16. Choose the correct answer for each question, and write the letter in the blank.

_____ 1. How many goats were part of this day?

    a. 1.   c. 3.

    b. 2.

_____ 2. Which animal made atonement for Aaron?

    a. Goat.   c. Dove.

    b. Sheep.   d. Bull.

_____ 3. The blood of the animal was sprinkled on the

    a. Ground.   c. People.

    b. Tabernacle.   d. Atonement cover (mercy seat).

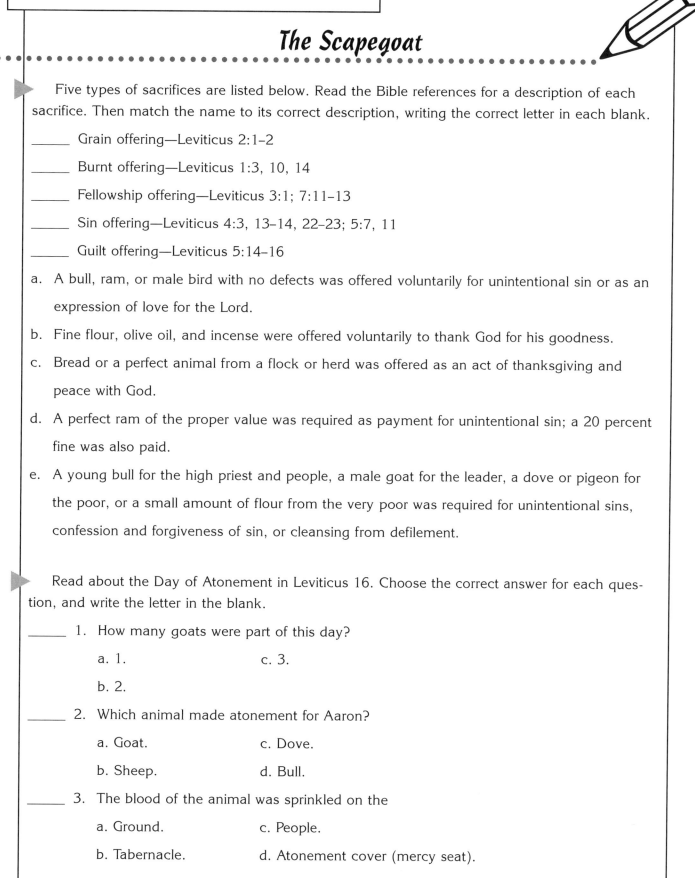

_____ 4. Which animal was slaughtered for the sins of the people?

       a. Goat.   c. Scapegoat.

       b. Bull.   d. Ram.

_____ 5. What happened to the scapegoat?

       a. He was killed.   c. He was led into the desert.

       b. Nothing.

6. What was the purpose of the Day of Atonement? _____

_____

7. Why did the high priest have to sacrifice for himself first of all? _____

_____

8. Why did the people have to fast (deny themselves) on the Day of Atonement? (See Leviticus 16:29–31.) _____

9. What was the purpose of the scapegoat? _____

10. Why do we no longer make animal and grain offerings? _____

_____

Feasting in the Lord

Read the references and fill in the chart for one of the feasts or special days.

Sabbath: Exodus 20:8–11; Leviticus 23:3

Sabbath Year: Leviticus 25:1–7

Passover: Exodus 12:1–14; Leviticus 23:5

Feast of Unleavened Bread: Exodus 12:15–20; Leviticus 23:6–8; Numbers 28:17–25

Feast of Firstfruits: Leviticus 23:9–14

Feast of Weeks: Leviticus 23:15–21; Deuteronomy 16:9–12

Feast of Trumpets: Leviticus 23:23–25; Numbers 29:1–6

Day of Atonement: Numbers 29:7–11; Leviticus 16

Feast of Tabernacles: Leviticus 23:33–43; Numbers 29:12–34; Deuteronomy 16:13–15

Year of Jubilee: Leviticus 25:8–55

Name of feast or special day:	
When was it?	
How long did it last?	
Purpose for feast or special day:	
What happened?	

Match the name of the celebration with its description.

_____ Every 50 years slaves were freed, debts were canceled, and property returned to its original owner.

_____ The Israelites lived in booths and recalled God's faithfulness in the desert.

_____ The Israelites remembered how God delivered them from slavery in Egypt.

_____ God's people recognized his goodness in the harvest.

_____ God's people worship him and rest from their daily work.

_____ This national day of mourning for sin was Israel's most important day.

_____ Held 50 days after Passover, this feast marked the beginning of the barley harvest.

_____ Israel presented itself before the Lord to ask his favor in the new year.

_____ Fields and Israel rested on this seventh year.

_____ This feast right after Passover reminded Israel of their hasty deliverance from Egypt.

a. Passover

b. Feast of Unleavened Bread

c. Feast of Firstfruits

d. Feast of Weeks

e. Day of Atonement

f. Sabbath Year

g. Feast of Trumpets

h. Feast of Tabernacles

i. Year of Jubilee

j. The Sabbath

Living the Law

First try to guess the answer for each of the following questions. Then answer them using the references found in Deuteronomy 18–25.

1. What could Israelites not sacrifice to the Lord? (18:10a)

   Guess: _____

   Answer: _____

2. If a man killed someone unintentionally, what could he do to protect himself against the avenger of the dead person? (19:1–7)

   Guess: _____

   Answer: _____

3. How many witnesses were necessary to convict a man accused of a crime? (19:15)

   Guess: _____

   Answer: _____

4. What happened to a lying witness? (19:16–21)

   Guess: _____

   Answer: _____

5. What happened to a rebellious son? (21:18–21)

   Guess: _____

   Answer: _____

6. What was true of anyone hung on a tree? (21:22–23)

   Guess: _____

   Answer: _____

7. If an Israelite found a stray animal whose owner lived far away, could he keep it? (22:2)

   Guess: _____

   Answer: _____

8. What happened to an adulterous man and woman? (22:22)

   Guess: _____

   Answer: _____

Unit 5, Lesson 16

9. Why did an Israelite have to be careful of what he or she promised? (23:21–23)

Guess: _____

Answer: _____

10. Why did Israelites have to be fair and just? (24:17–18)

Guess: _____

Answer: _____

11. Was a farmer to keep all the crops of his fields and vineyards? (24:19–22) Explain.

Guess: _____

Answer: _____

_____

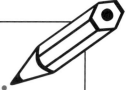

The Fire Did It!

Use Exodus 32 to help you fill in the blanks.

The people were tired of waiting for Moses, so they said to _____, "Come, make

us _____ who will go before us."

He answered them, "Bring your _____ earrings to me." So all the people took

them off and brought them to Aaron. He made them into an idol cast in the shape of a

_____. The people said "These are your _____, O Israel, who brought

you out of _____."

Then Aaron built an _____ in front of the calf and announced, "Tomorrow there

will be a _____ to the Lord." So the following day the people rose up early to present

_____ to their idol. Then they _____ and _____ and par-

tied.

God told Moses to go down to Israel because they were sacrificing to an idol. He described

Israel as a _____ people. He wanted to _____ them.

Moses pleaded with God. He reminded God what the _____ would say if they

heard the Lord had struck Israel down in the desert. He also reminded the Lord of the

_____ he had made to _____ and _____ and

_____ to make their _____ as numerous as the stars. God relented and

turned from his anger. But Moses burned with anger when he approached the camp and saw the

_____ and the people _____. He threw down the two

_____ of the Law, breaking them into pieces. Then he took the calf and

_____ it. Next he ground it to a _____, and scattered it on the

_____, and made the Israelites _____ it. When Moses asked Aaron to

explain what had happened, Aaron replied, "They gave me the gold, and I threw it into the fire,

and _____!"

The people were running wild. So Moses stood at the entrance to the camp and said,

"Whoever is for the _____, come to me." And all of the _____ came to

him. That day the Levites _____ about three thousand of the people. Because of

their obedient response to Moses, the _____ were set apart to the Lord that day.

The next day Moses told the people, "You have committed a great _____. But now I will go up to the _____; perhaps I can make _____ for your sin."

Then Moses pleaded with the Lord. He asked God to _____ his name from God's

book if God could not forgive the people. God responded by punishing the people with a

_____.

The Fire Did It!

Exodus 33 and 34 reveal some important patterns about God and his relationship with Moses and the people of Israel. Read the passages from Exodus and write a brief summary to complete the chart below.

	Exodus 33	Exodus 34
God's anger	verses 1–3	verse 7
Moses the mediator	verses 12–13, 15–16	verses 8–9
God's mercy	verses 14, 17	verses 6, 10
God's glory	verses 19–23	verses 29–32

1. God cannot tolerate anything we put ahead of him. What kind of gods do people worship today? What does God think of them? _____

_____

2. What future mediator would be more powerful than Moses, and how did he secure God's mercy for all of us? _____

_____

3. Why was Moses' face radiant? Have you ever seen someone's face that radiated the joy of knowing God? What was it like? _____

_____

The Journey to Canaan

Have you ever seen a stretch of sand that has been blown by the wind? The wind shapes the tiny grains into beautiful wavelike patterns. On their journey across the desert to Canaan, the Israelites may have seen some of these natural wonders.

The Israelites also left patterns as they traveled. The people sinned and rebelled over and over again. But God stayed with them in his own pattern. God is holy and demands holy behavior from his people, so he corrected them. God also is full of love and grace. God repeatedly kept his promises to bless the Israelites and take care of them.

As you study the Israelites' journey to Canaan, use the chart below to track the patterns in the sand.

Bible Reference	People's Action	Moses' Action	God's Judgment	God's Blessing
Numbers 11				
Numbers 12				
Numbers 13–14				

Bible Reference	People's Action	Moses' Action	God's Judgment	God's Blessing
Numbers 16-17				
Numbers 20:1-21				
Numbers 21:4-9				
Numbers 25				

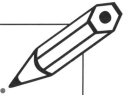

Pails of Quail

▶ This story from the Bible begins with these words: "Now the people complained." God heard their complaints and gave them what they wanted—pails and pails of quail meat. Read Numbers 11, and then complete this study guide to discover how we should be content with what God gives us.

1. Look up the word *rabble* in the dictionary. In your own words, write down the definition.

   _____

   _____

▶ Read each statement below and decide whether it is true or false. Correct the false statements.

_____ 1. God had the Levites kill the Israelites when they complained.

   _____

_____ 2. The Israelites believed their lives were better in Egypt.

   _____

_____ 3. The people quietly complained to family members about the boring diet of manna.

   _____

_____ 4. Moses complained to God about having to deal with the complaining people.

   _____

_____ 5. God appointed 40 elders to help Moses govern Israel.

   _____

_____ 6. The elders prophesied, which showed that God's Spirit rested on them.

   _____

_____ 7. Joshua was happy about the prophesying elders.

   _____

_____ 8. Moses was jealous that God's Spirit was upon others.

   _____

_____ 9. Moses and the elders gave the people quail to eat.

   _____

_____ 10. Not everyone had enough meat to eat.

   _____

_____ 11. God was pleased that the people had craved meat.

   _____

Unit 6, Lesson 1

►Thinking It Over

1. Why do you think God gave Israel the meat they craved? _____
    _____

2. Give an example of something you might demand that would end up hurting you if God gave in
    to your demand. _____
    _____

3. What promise does Jesus give us about what we need? Read Matthew 6:25–34. _____
    _____

4. I want to feel more content about _____
    _____

    I can entrust this to the Lord because _____
    _____

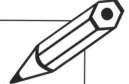

Family Feud

The green-eyed monster.

Green with envy.

The grass is always greener on the other side of the fence.

▶How Green Are You?

The color green is often connected with jealousy and envy. We all have "green" feelings once in a while. Look at the rating scale below, and then read each example. Imagine yourself in that situation and write down the number that best matches how "green" you would feel.

Rating:

0   not one bit jealous

1   hardly jealous at all

2   somewhat jealous

3   very jealous

4   screaming "green" all over

_____ 1. Your parents give your brother or sister credit for something that you did.

_____ 2. A classmate comes to school wearing the newest style of clothes or shoes, and you're stuck with your old clothes.

_____ 3. Your teacher chooses another student to be the leader even though that person has been the leader many times.

_____ 4. The person who sits next to you always seems to get better grades than you.

_____ 5. Your parents praise your brother or sister for their talents or accomplishments.

_____ 6. You find out that you weren't invited to a party or event that many of your friends are going to.

_____ 7. Other people always seem to have better treats in their lunches.

_____ 8. The other boys or girls in your class talk in a group but don't include you.

Name _____

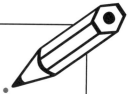

Family Feud

Miriam and Aaron were jealous of Moses' special friendship with God. They thought that they should get more credit for all the things they did. They started to talk against their own brother, stirring up trouble in their family and in the family of God. Read Numbers 12 to answer the questions about this sad family feud.

1. Did Moses speak up in his own defense? What does this show about him? _____
   _____

2. State in your own words what God said was special about Moses in verses 6–8. _____
   _____
   _____

3. Why was God angry with Miriam and Aaron? _____
   _____
   _____
   _____

4. Describe Miriam's punishment. How did the punishment fit her crime? _____
   _____
   _____
   _____
   _____

5. How did Miriam's brothers respond to her punishment? _____
   _____
   _____

6. What are some ways students your age can show humility at school? Write a list of six to ten simple actions that show humility. _____
   _____
   _____

7. Observe your classmates over the next day or two. Look for someone doing one of the actions on your list or something else that shows humility. Write down who you saw and what that person did. _____
   _____
   _____

Name _____

Ten against Two

This is an important mission. The nation's welfare rests on your work. If you accept this assignment, you may find yourself in great danger. You will be going undercover into a foreign country. For security reasons, the rest of your instructions are given in code. Decipher the messages to discover the details of your assignment.

You must take with you good and trustworthy fellow spies. There will be this many spies in all:

$$\frac{(9 \times 8)}{6} = \boxed{}$$

Use the code given below to find out what information to obtain.

☐☐☐☐ ☐☐ ☐☐☐ ☐☐☐☐ ☐☐☐☐?
23 8 1 20 9 19 20 8 5 12 1 14 4 12 9 11 5

☐☐☐ ☐☐☐☐☐ ☐☐☐ ☐☐☐☐☐☐ ☐☐ ☐☐☐☐?
1 18 5 20 8 5 18 5 6 5 23 16 5 15 16 12 5 15 18 13 1 14 25

☐☐☐ ☐☐☐☐ ☐☐☐☐☐☐ ☐☐☐☐☐☐☐ ☐☐ ☐☐☐☐?
1 18 5 20 8 5 16 5 15 16 12 5 19 20 18 15 14 7 15 18 23 5 1 11

☐☐☐☐ ☐☐☐ ☐☐☐☐☐ ☐☐☐☐?
23 8 1 20 1 18 5 20 8 5 20 15 23 14 19 12 9 11 5

☐☐ ☐☐☐ ☐☐☐☐☐ ☐☐☐☐ ☐☐☐☐☐?
4 15 20 8 5 20 15 23 14 19 8 1 22 5 23 1 12 12 19

☐☐☐ ☐☐ ☐☐☐ ☐☐☐☐?
8 15 23 9 19 20 8 5 19 15 9 12

☐☐☐☐ ☐☐☐☐☐ ☐☐☐ ☐☐☐☐☐ ☐☐☐☐☐☐?
23 8 1 20 11 9 14 4 15 6 6 18 21 9 20 7 18 15 23 19 20 8 5 18 5

Your mission should take this many days to complete:

$$\frac{(16 \times 5)}{2} = \boxed{}$$

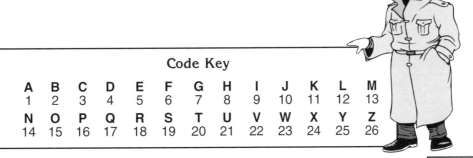

Code Key												
A	**B**	**C**	**D**	**E**	**F**	**G**	**H**	**I**	**J**	**K**	**L**	**M**
1	2	3	4	5	6	7	8	9	10	11	12	13
N	**O**	**P**	**Q**	**R**	**S**	**T**	**U**	**V**	**W**	**X**	**Y**	**Z**
14	15	16	17	18	19	20	21	22	23	24	25	26

Unit 6, Lesson 3

121

Report:

Now that you have completed your mission, make two lists. On one list write all of the good things that you discovered about Canaan. On the other write what was bad about the land.

Good Things in the Land of Canaan	Bad Things in the Land of Canaan

Recommendation:

You've written your report and talked to your fellow spies. Now it's time to make recommendations. Write what the majority recommends that the nation do. Also write the other opinion down as the minority recommendation, and give the names of the spies with that view.

Majority Recommendation: _____

_____

_____

Minority Recommendation: _____

_____

_____

Who Is Holy?

Each of the sentences below summarizes part of the story of Korah's rebellion. Read Numbers 16, and then number the sentences in the order that they happened in the story.

_____ Korah, Dathan, and Abiram (plus 250 other leaders) rose up against Moses.

_____ Moses pleaded with God to spare the life of the rebels.

_____ The Lord destroyed another 14,700 Israelites with a plague.

_____ The bronze censors were hammered into sheets to overlay the altar.

_____ The earth swallowed Dathan, Abiram, and the families of the three rebels.

_____ Moses told the rebels to bring their censers to the Tent of Meeting.

_____ Fire burned up the 250 men offering the incense.

_____ The whole Israelite community accused Moses and Aaron of murder.

_____ Aaron ran through the camp with his censer and the plague stopped.

_____ Dathan and Abiram refused to come to the Tent of Meeting, but Korah and his followers came.

Name _____

More Rebellions and Punishments

The Israelites were coming to the end of their travels in the desert. Use this activity to discover more about the major roadblock Edom put in their way. Refer to Numbers 20:14–21 and the map below to answer the questions.

1. What did Moses' messengers tell the king of Edom (Numbers 20:14–17, 19)?

_____
_____
_____

2. What was Edom's reply (Numbers 20:18, 20a)? _____
_____
_____

4. What did the Edomites finally do (Numbers 20:20b)? _____
_____
_____
_____

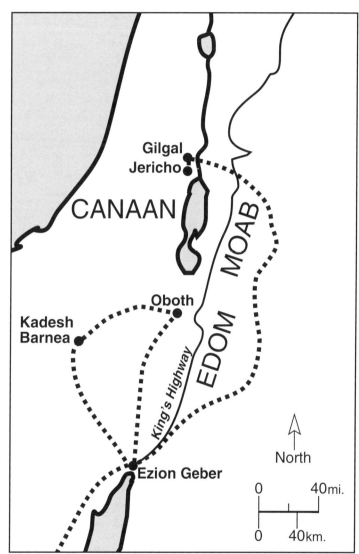

5. The Israelites' request to the king of Edom was for passage on the king's highway, an easier route directly through Edom to Canaan. Using the key on the map, estimate about how many miles the Israelites would have traveled if they could have taken the king's highway starting near what may have been the town of Oboth. _____

6. The Israelites now had to go around Edom. Starting again from the town of Oboth, use the map and the key again to estimate about how far the Israelites had to travel around.

_____

The Last Stage of the Journey

▶ Pretend that you are an Israelite. You were a small child when you left with your parents on the exodus from Egypt. You grew up camping in a tent in the desert. Now you are 40–50 years old. Finish the entry in your diary.

My name is _____. I've been living in a tent in the desert all of my life. These are the things that I don't like about this life and the things that I'm looking forward to in the Promised Land:

Balak, Balaam, a Burro, and a Blessing

Read about Balak, Balaam, the burro, and the blessings in Numbers 22–25. Answer the questions below as you discover more about bossy Balak, baffled Balaam, the balking burro, and the bountiful blessings.

1. What made Balak, the king of Moab, so afraid of the Israelites? (See also Numbers 21:21–35.)
   _____

2. King Balak sent for Balaam, a diviner (a person who practices magic and fortune telling) who lived far to the north near the Euphrates River. What did he want Balaam to do? _____
   _____

3. What did Balaam tell the princes who brought Balak's message? _____
   _____

4. What did Balak do when he heard Balaam's reply? _____
   _____

5. What were the second instructions God gave to Balaam? _____
   _____

6. Why do you think the angel tried to stop Balaam three times when God had said Balaam could go? _____

7. What did Balaam do three times that defeated King Balak? _____
   _____

8. In Balaam's fourth prophecy he saw a star, a scepter, and a ruler who would conquer all evil. Read Numbers 24:17–19. Whose coming do you think Balaam was prophesying? _____
   _____

9. What happened to the Israelites who began to worship Baal? _____

10. What did one Israelite have the nerve to do? _____
    _____

11. Evidently a plague came over the Israelites because of his sin. How was the plague stopped?
    _____

12. How many died in the plague? _____

13. What "royal grant" covenant did God make with Phinehas (Aaron's grandson) as a reward for his action? _____

14. How were the Israelites to treat the Midianites from then on? _____

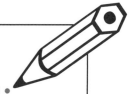

Name _____

Say It Again

The Book of Deuteronomy records Moses' final words to the Israelite people before they entered the Promised Land. The series of speeches covers both the law and history of God and his people. The following four sections cover most of the Book of Deuteronomy. Read each statement and the Bible reference, and then decide whether the statement is true (T) or false (F). If the answer is false, correct it.

▶ Basic Commandments—Deuteronomy 5–11

_____ 1. Israel could make treaties with the nations living in Canaan. (7:2) _____

_____

_____ 2. God vowed to destroy Israel if it forgot him and followed other gods. (8:19) _____

_____

_____ 3. God chose Israel because it was a large and strong people. (7:7–8) _____

_____

_____ 4. Israel was commanded to remember its past. (11:1–7) _____

_____

▶ Detailed Laws—Deuteronomy 12–26

_____ 5. When the Israelites ate meat, they could not eat the blood. (12:16) _____

_____

_____ 6. The Israelites had to worship God differently than the heathens worshiped their gods. (12:29–31) _____

_____

_____ 7. The Israelites could eat any animal. (14:3–21) _____

_____

_____ 8. Israelite widows and orphans had to steal in order to make a living. (14:29) _____

_____

_____ 9. Debts were canceled every ten years. (15:1–6) _____

_____

_____ 10. The Israelites were to give freely to the poor. (15:7–8) _____

_____

_____ 11. Every Israelite man had to give the same gift to the Lord three times a year. (16:16–17)

_____

_____

_____ 12. Judges could show partiality toward people. (16:19) _____

_____

_____ 13. An Israelite bowing down to the moon had to be killed. (17:2–5) _____

_____

_____ 14. The people were to accept the decisions of priests and judges. (17:8–11) _____

_____

_____ 15. The Levites could live on the Israelites' offerings. (18:1) _____

_____

Curses and Blessings—Deuteronomy 27–30

_____ 16. When they were finally in the Promised Land, six of the tribes were to stand on Mount Gerizim to pronounce blessings, and the other six were to stand on Mount Ebal to pronounce curses. (27:11–13) _____

_____

_____ 17. Israelites who did not live according to the law were cursed. (27:26) _____

_____

_____ 18. God would bless his people no matter how they lived (28:1–2) _____

_____

_____ 19. If the people did not obey God's commands, curses would come upon them. (28:15)

_____

_____ 20. Heaven and earth were witnesses of this covenant between God and his people. (30:19)

_____

The Covenant in Safekeeping—Deuteronomy 31

_____ 21. God promised that he would never leave or forsake Israel. (31:6) _____

_____

_____ 22. The priests received the law from Moses. (31:9) _____

_____

_____ 23. The children were not required to hear the law or fear the Lord. (31:13) _____

_____

_____ 24. Moses predicted that the people of Israel would obey his commands. (31:28–29)

_____

_____

The End of the Beginning

Psalm 106:1–33 tells about some of the events in the life of Moses and the people of Israel. The poet tells of God's faithfulness and the Israelites' faithlessness. Read each section of Psalm 106 listed below. Then tell what story the psalmist is describing in each of these sections. After reading all of the sections, number the events in the order that they happened.

Section of Psalm 106	Event	The Order of Events
verses 7–12		
verses 13–15		
verses 16–18		
verses 19–23		
verses 24–27		
verses 28–31		
verses 32–33		

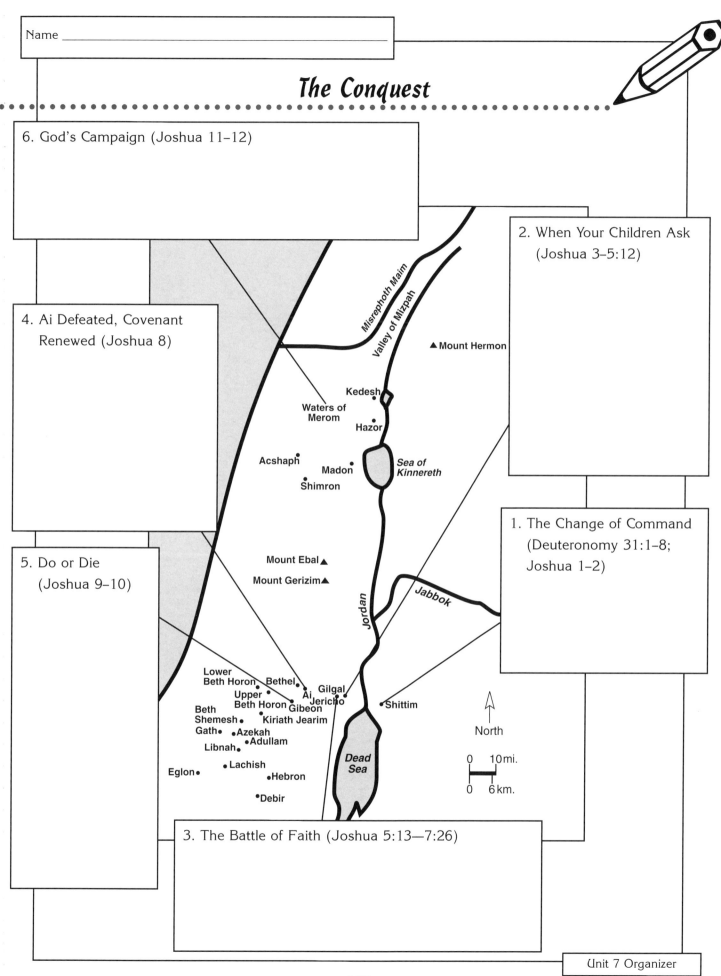

Name _____

The Conquest

6. God's Campaign (Joshua 11–12)

2. When Your Children Ask (Joshua 3–5:12)

4. Ai Defeated, Covenant Renewed (Joshua 8)

5. Do or Die (Joshua 9–10)

1. The Change of Command (Deuteronomy 31:1–8; Joshua 1–2)

3. The Battle of Faith (Joshua 5:13—7:26)

Misrephoth Maim

Valley of Mizpah

▲ Mount Hermon

Kedesh

Waters of Merom

Hazor

Acshaph

Madon

Sea of Kinnereth

Shimron

Mount Ebal ▲

Mount Gerizim ▲

Jordan

Jabbok

Lower Beth Horon

Bethel

Ai

Gilgal

Upper Beth Horon

Gibeon

Jericho

Shittim

Beth Shemesh

Kiriath Jearim

Gath

Azekah

Adullam

Libnah

Eglon

Lachish

Dead Sea

Hebron

Debir

North

0   10 mi.

0   6 km.

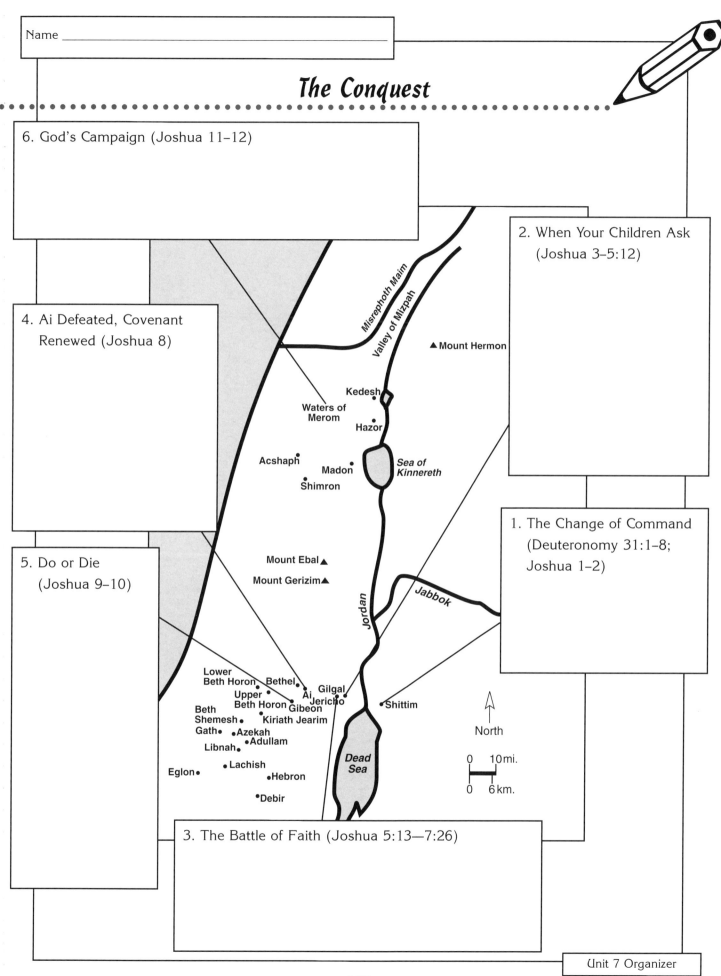

Name _____

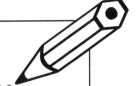

The Change of Command

Moses would not be permitted to lead God's people into the Promised Land. Joshua, Moses' longtime assistant, would take over as Israel's next leader.

1. Read what Moses told the people and Joshua in Deuteronomy 31:1–8. Put an X in front of the command or words of encouragement that Moses spoke to Joshua.

   _____ Don't be a chicken.

   _____ Be strong and courageous.

   _____ God is right behind you all the way.

   _____ Do not be discouraged.

   _____ The Lord himself will go before you.

   _____ You must divide the land among the Israelites.

   _____ God will never leave or forsake you.

   _____ Good luck!

   _____ Do not be afraid.

   _____ Look out for yourself.

2. Read what the Lord commanded Joshua in Joshua 1:1–9. In these verses one command is repeated three times. Write the command. Why do you think it is mentioned three times?

   _____

   _____

   _____

3. What do you think God meant when he told Joshua to meditate on the law day and night?

   _____

   _____

   _____

4. Even though Joshua was leading the people, was there someone he was supposed to follow? Who? _____

   _____

The Change of Command

Joshua was born and raised as a child of God. Rahab was grown and leading a sinful life when she first heard about God. Yet both of these people are great examples of faith. Think about Joshua taking Moses' place as leader of God's people and about Rahab saving two Israelite spies and helping God's people take the Promised Land. Answer the following questions two times—once for Joshua and once for Rahab—as you study how these two people lived their faith.

	Joshua	Rahab
How did this person know about God?		
What promises did this person receive?		
How did this person show strength and courage?		
Who did this person place confidence in?		
What do you admire about this person?		

When Your Children Ask

The events from Joshua 3 and 4 are listed below, but they are in the wrong order. Unscramble the story by numbering the events in the right order. If you're not sure, look at Joshua 3–5:12. Have a partner check your work. Then cut along the lines and glue the events in the correct order on a separate sheet of paper.

_____   Twelve stones were set up as a memorial at Gilgal.

_____   Twelve men were chosen, one from each tribe.

_____   The water of the Jordan River started flowing again.

_____   The ark and priests stood on dry ground in the middle of the Jordan River as Israel crossed.

_____   Joshua taught Israel about the purpose of the memorial.

_____   Twelve men took one stone each from the middle of the river where the priests were standing.

_____   God stopped the river's flow when the priests' feet touched the water.

_____   Joshua told the priests to come up out of the Jordan River.

_____   Joshua told the people that they would know God was with them.

Name _____

Ai Defeated, Covenant Renewed

▶ The little town of Ai had defeated Israel once. But this time God was with his people. Read Joshua 8:1–29. Follow the clever battle plan that tricked Ai. Fill in the blanks below with the correct answers.

1. God told Joshua to do to Ai and its king as Joshua had done to _____ and its king.

2. Unlike at Jericho, the Israelites were allowed to carry off Ai's _____ and _____ for themselves.

3. God told Joshua to set an _____ behind the city.

4. The _____ of Ai were lured from their city by _____ and his supposedly fleeing men.

5. Another group of men waited between _____ and Ai.

6. When Joshua held out his _____, the city was ambushed by the second group of Israelites and was set on fire.

7. _____ men and women of Ai fell that day.

▶ Before the Israelites entered the Promised Land, Moses planned a ceremony for the people to perform to remind them of God's covenant and the words of his law. Read Joshua 8:30–35 and then answer the following questions.

1. Read Genesis 12:6–7. What promise to Abraham had been fulfilled at this point in Israelite history? _____

_____

2. The city of Shechem was located at the foot of Mount Ebal. Why was Mount Ebal an appropriate place for Joshua to build an altar to God? _____

_____

_____

3. Sketch the scene of the ceremony as you imagine it looked.

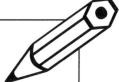

Do or Die

▶ Alarmed by the success of the Israelites, one city resorted to a ruse. They respected the Israelite power and the power of their God, but they were not converted to the faith as Rahab was. They decided to trick Joshua and his men in order to avoid fighting them. Read Joshua 9 to find out more about their trick.

1. Who tricked the Israelites? _____

2. How did they trick the Israelites? _____

_____

_____

3. What mistake did the Israelites make? _____

_____

4. What was the result? _____

_____

5. What did Israel do when they discovered the trick? _____

_____

▶ The treaty that the Gibeonites signed with the Israelites didn't keep them out of trouble. Now their former friends felt betrayed and were angry with them. Five of the Amorite kings decided to attack Gibeon. Read Joshua 10:5–28. Then read the statements below. Decide whether each statement is true or false. Cross out the false statements.

_____ Gibeon joined the Amorite kings fighting against Israel.

_____ God threw the enemy into confusion and defeated them.

_____ Hail killed more enemies than Israelite swords did.

_____ The sun stood still while the battle raged.

_____ The five kings died in the cave of Makkedah.

_____ Joshua didn't leave any survivors in the cities he conquered.

_____ Joshua won all of his battles because God was with him.

_____ Joshua's camp was near a memorial.

_____ In one campaign Joshua conquered the whole region.

Name _____

God's Campaign

The Israelites' strategy of gaining control of the Promised Land seems brilliant. Joshua was a great leader, but it was God who gave Israel the victory. Use colored pencils to show the stages of the conquest on the map below. Color the boxes of the key to show what color you used for each stage.

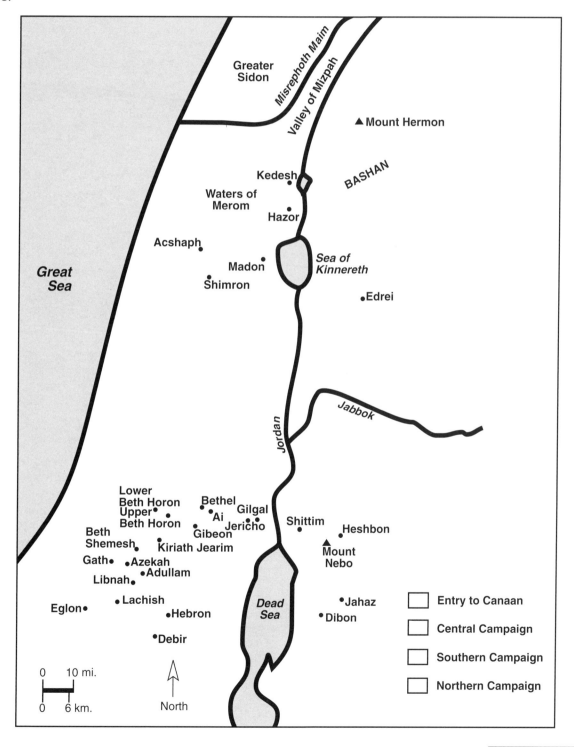

☐ Entry to Canaan

☐ Central Campaign

☐ Southern Campaign

☐ Northern Campaign

God's Campaign

Only the northern part of Canaan was left for the Israelites to conquer. Read about the northern campaign in Joshua 11:1–15. After studying the last battles for the Promised Land, answer the questions below.

1. What challenges did Israel face in these battles? _____

   _____

2. What was the outcome? _____

   _____

3. What did Joshua do in obedience to God's directions? (See verses 9–11.) _____

   _____

4. To what extent did Joshua obey God? (See verse 15.) _____

   _____

Joshua 12 lists the victories of the Israelites. Verses 9–24 list the kings of 31 places that Israel defeated. Each place is included in the word search below. Find them all to gain your own victory over this puzzle.

G	O	Y	I	M	H	E	P	H	E	R	H	O	Y	H
L	I	B	N	A	H	A	R	R	N	C	O	M	T	M
T	I	R	Z	A	H	E	I	O	A	D	A	U	A	N
H	A	Z	O	R	D	B	R	N	D	E	M	L	O	L
C	A	K	O	E	E	B	A	I	N	R	L	R	Z	Y
J	M	S	G	D	E	A	G	K	A	U	A	K	Y	B
Q	E	A	C	H	T	E	O	J	D	H	R	E	P	O
L	J	R	K	H	M	J	M	A	S	L	G	D	A	R
S	A	E	U	K	A	I	E	A	F	L	E	E	I	T
B	H	C	R	S	E	P	L	G	H	T	Z	S	H	A
P	E	I	H	I	A	D	H	A	L	W	E	H	O	P
K	S	T	M	I	C	L	A	S	P	O	R	O	R	P
C	T	C	H	R	S	H	E	H	R	H	N	D	M	U
K	I	U	D	E	O	H	O	M	N	F	E	I	A	A
M	A	D	O	N	L	N	A	R	A	D	Z	K	H	H

Where Do I Go?

The tribes of Israel finally had a permanent home. Each tribe received land according to its inheritance. Find out which tribes settled where by checking out a Bible map. Label the areas of land marked below with the name of the tribe it belonged to. Color each tribe's land a different color.

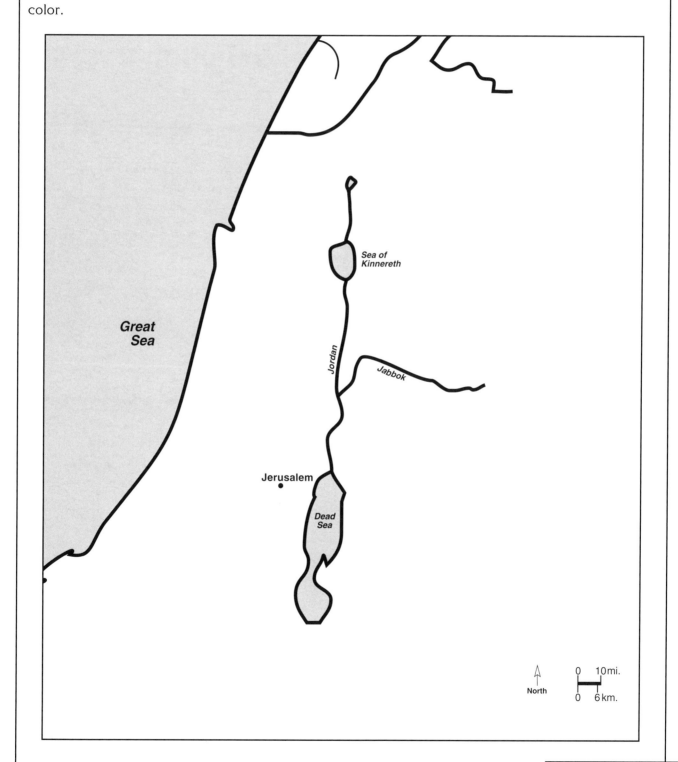

Where Do I Go?

From the time that he and Joshua were spies on the original foray into the Promised Land, Caleb had unwavering faith in God's promise to deliver the land into the hands of the Israelites. Read Joshua 14:6–15 to find out about Caleb now that Israel had entered the Promised Land.

Why was Caleb given Hebron as his inheritance? _____

_____

In some parts of Israel, though, the people were unable to overcome the Canaanites. Read about these failures in the passages below. Then list the tribe mentioned, and what people, city, or cities they were unable to overcome.

Scripture	Tribe	People/City/Cities
Joshua 15:63		
Joshua 16:5, 10		
Joshua 17:11–13		

What kinds of problems do you think the Israelites might face with these Canaanites who were left in their land? _____

_____

_____

Where Do I Go?

land	faithfulness	gods
Throw	Egypt	serve
forefathers	fear	Now
undesirable	Lord	River
me	choose	household
day	living	Amorites

Where Do I Go?

Joshua 24:14–15

[_____] [_____] the Lord and [_____]

him with all [_____] . [_____] away the

[_____] your [_____] worshiped beyond the River

and in [_____] , and serve the [_____] . But if

serving the Lord seems [_____] to you, then

[_____] for yourselves this [_____] whom you will

serve, whether the gods your forefathers served beyond the

[_____] , or the gods of the [_____] , in whose

[_____] you are [_____] . But as for

[_____] and my [_____] , we will serve the Lord.

But It Was an Accident!

God wanted to make sure that justice would be done. That's why he assigned six cities as cities of refuge. Read about these cities in Joshua 20, and then read the statements below. Number the statements in the correct chronological order.

_____ The person stayed in the city until a trial was held or the high priest died.

_____ He was admitted to the city and lived there.

_____ When a person killed someone accidentally, he could flee to a city of refuge.

_____ He then stated his case to the elders at the city gate.

_____ If he was found innocent or the high priest died, he could return to his own home town.

_____ If the avenger of blood arrived, the person's life would be protected.

Now meet with some of your classmates and use your imaginations. Think of a story you could act out for the class that would show how the cities of refuge worked.

_____

_____

_____

_____

_____

_____

_____

_____

_____

_____

_____

_____

_____

_____

_____

_____

_____

_____

_____

Joshua's Farewell

Before he died, Joshua had some important things to say to the Israelites. In his farewell speech he recalled the promises that God had kept for his people. He reminded them of God's commands, and he once again spoke the warnings attached to God's promises. Read Joshua 23. In the boxes below list the promises, commands, and warnings from Joshua's farewell address.

Promises	
Commands	
Warnings	

Name _____

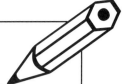

Joshua's Farewell

▶ The following list shows some of the key events in Israel's history. Read through the list silently. Then number the events in the correct chronological order. If you can't remember, check out Joshua 24:1–13, where Joshua reminded the people of their past.

_____ God gave Israel a rich, wealthy land.

_____ God led Abraham to Canaan and gave him many descendants.

_____ God brought Israel out of Egypt and drowned the Egyptians.

_____ God defeated Jericho and the other inhabitants of Canaan.

_____ God led Israel through the desert and gave them victory over the Amorites.

_____ God led Jacob and his family to Egypt. Esau went to Seir.

_____ God caused Balaam to bless Israel instead of cursing them.

▶ Write out Israel's choice from Joshua 24:24.

_____

_____

Joshua's Farewell

Think back on the history of your own life: caring parents, good friends, kind teachers, and lessons that were hard to learn. Maybe these things have shown you how God cares for you or how he wants you to live. Try to think of one or two events from the years listed. Then follow these steps to complete this activity.

1. For each section labeled with an age, write at least one thing you remember from that time in your life and what you learned from it.

2. Think about the future. Ask yourself, "Whom am I serving?" Write your answer in the section labeled "My Choice."

3. Cut out the boxes, and glue them in order from top to bottom on the back of your stone witness sheet.

Birth to Five Years Old

Five to Nine Years Old

Nine Years Old to Today

My Choice

Name _____

The Judges and Ruth

"Whenever the Lord raised up a judge for them, he was with the judge and saved them out of the hands of their enemies as long as the judge lived; for the Lord had compassion on them as they groaned under those who oppressed and afflicted them."

—Judges 2:18

Major Judges	Minor Judges

Unit 8 Organizer 1

◀ **Profile of a Judge**

Name: _____

Years of leading Israel: _____

Best known for: _____

_____

_____

Delivered Israel from: _____

_____

_____

Israel was delivered when: _____

_____

Draw a symbol for this judge.

◀ **Profile of a Judge**

Name: _____

Years of leading Israel: _____

Best known for: _____

_____

_____

Delivered Israel from: _____

_____

_____

Israel was delivered when: _____

_____

Draw a symbol for this judge.

Profile of a Judge

Name: _____

Years of leading Israel: _____

Best known for: _____

_____

_____

Delivered Israel from: _____

_____

Israel was delivered when: _____

_____

_____

Draw a symbol for this judge.

_____

-- fold --

Profile of a Judge

Name: _____

Years of leading Israel: _____

Best known for: _____

_____

_____

_____

Delivered Israel from: _____

_____

Israel was delivered when: _____

_____

Draw a symbol for this judge.

_____

_____

Unit 8 Organizer 2

169

Profile of a Judge ◄

Name: _____

Years of leading Israel: _____

Best known for: _____
_____
_____
_____

Delivered Israel from: _____
_____

Israel was delivered when: _____
_____

Draw a symbol for this judge.

Profile of a Judge ◄

Name: _____

Years of leading Israel: _____

Best known for: _____
_____
_____
_____

Delivered Israel from: _____
_____

Israel was delivered when: _____

Draw a symbol for this judge.

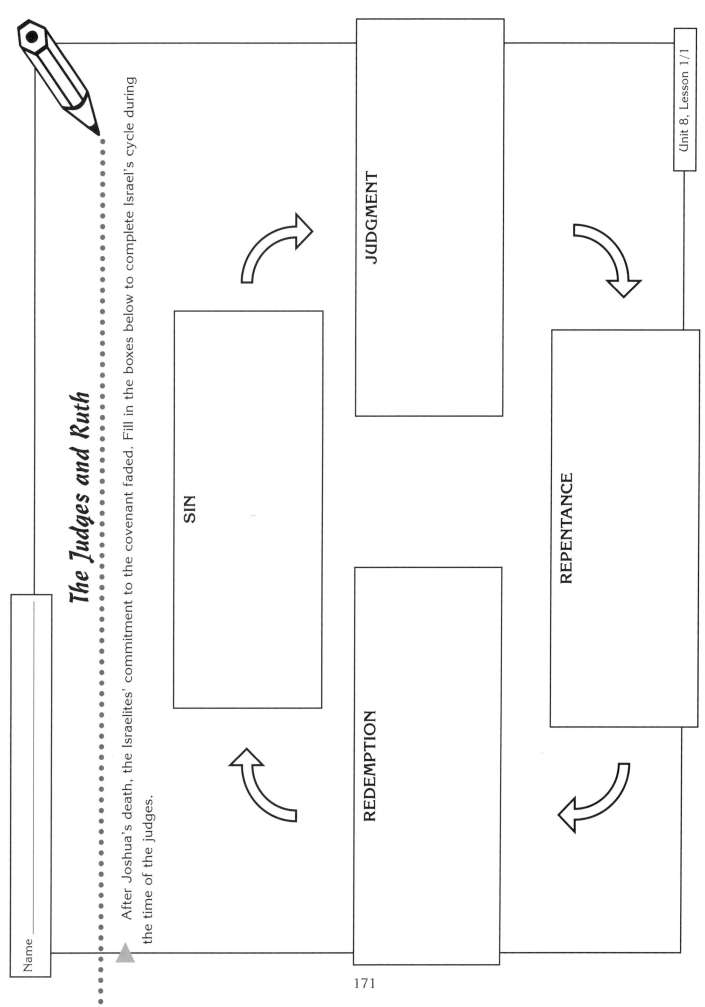

Name _____

The Judges and Ruth

After Joshua's death, the Israelites' commitment to the covenant faded. Fill in the boxes below to complete Israel's cycle during the time of the judges.

SIN

JUDGMENT

REDEMPTION

REPENTANCE

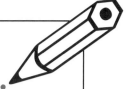

Round and Round

In each paragraph you'll find the words needed to complete the crossword puzzles. Read the entire paragraph first. Then use the clues to complete the puzzle.

The Philistines

The Philistines were great warriors. Because they originally came by boat from lands around the Mediterranean Sea, they were called the sea people. They fought against Egypt but could not conquer it, so they settled along the coast of Canaan. The Philistines set up five city-states of kingdoms in Palestine. They were Ashdod, Gaza, Gath, Ekron, and Ashkelon. The Philistines built smelting furnaces in order to make iron weapons. This gave them an advantage in battle. One of the gods they worshiped was named Dagon.

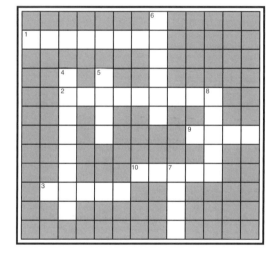

Clues

1. Military men
2. A name for people who travel by water
3. A shoreline
4–8. Names of five Philistine city-states
9. A kind of metal
10. One of the Philistine gods

The Moabites

The Moabites occupied the land east of the Dead Sea, also called the Salt Sea. The Moabites worshiped Chemosh and other gods. They sacrificed animals to their gods. One of their kings during the period of the judges was King Eglon. The Moabites were powerful. Under Eglon they invaded Israel and took control of the land west of the Jordan River as far as the city of Jericho.

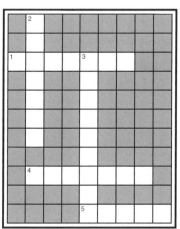

Clues

1. Another name for the Salt Sea
2. Name of a Moabite god
3. A ritual of worship
4. The city where the walls fell down
5. Name of a Moabite king during the period of the judges

The Canaanites

Many different people were called Canaanites. Generally, Canaanites were the people who occupied the land north of Philistia. The Canaanites fought using chariots. They were an agricultural people. They worshiped Baal and Ashtoreth, a god and goddess of fertility. Each town had a different name for each of the gods.

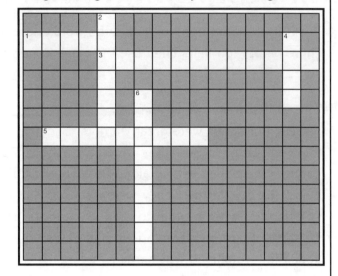

Clues

1. The opposite direction of south
2. A two-wheeled vehicle sometimes used in war
3. Having to do with farming
4. A Canaanite god
5. A Canaanite goddess
6. Ashtoreth and Baal were these types of gods

The Midianites

The Midianites were a desert people who lived south of Moab. These people rode fast camels and swiftly attacked their enemies. They also mined copper. The Midianites were descendants of Keturah and Abraham. Moses' wife was a Midianite.

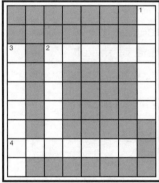

Clues

1. Hot, dry land
2. Across. Humped animals ridden by the Midianites
2. Pennies are made of this metal.
3–4. Ancestors of the Midianites

The Ammonites

The Ammonites occupied the land northeast of the Salt Sea, just north of Moab. The Ammonites were descendants of Lot. They worshiped a god called Molech and made burnt offerings of children to him. Several of Israel's judges, including Jephthah and Ehud, fought against the Ammonites.

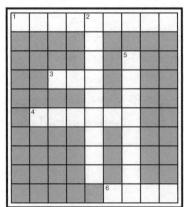

Clues

1. People living just north of Moab
2. Direction of the Ammonites land in relation to the Salt Sea
3. Abraham's nephew
4. Human sacrifices were made to this god.
5–6. Two of Israel's judges who fought against the Ammonites.

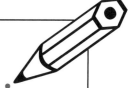

Name _____

The Wheel Spins

When the sinful Israelites cried to the Lord in distress and repentance, he listened and sent judges to deliver his people. Read about the first three deliverers in Judges 3, and answer the questions.

Judges 3:7–11

1. What did the Israelites do that displeased God? _____

2. To whom did God "sell" the Israelites? _____

3. How long did God allow this king to discipline Israel? _____
   _____

4. Whom did God send to rescue his children? _____
   _____

5. How did Othniel deliver Israel from the Canaanites? _____
   _____

Judges 3:12–30

7. *Ehud* means "one who praises." Why was that a fitting name for this judge? _____
   _____

8. Describe the king of the Moabites. _____

9. Describe the judge's successful plan to kill the king. _____
   _____

10. What was the escape plan? _____
    _____

11. Do you think that God approved of the murder of Eglon? _____
    _____
    _____

Judges 3:31

12. Describe Israel's deliverance under Shamgar. _____

13. What was unusual about Shamgar's methods? _____

A Thunderbolt, a Faithful Bee, and a Mountain Goat

▶ **God's Victory**

1. Read Deborah's victory song in Judges 5. Write down the verses in which you find the following.

   Praise was first given to God. _____

   Deborah called herself a mother in Israel. _____

   The groups who fought were honored. _____

   Those who didn't fight were scolded. _____

   The battle's history was retold. _____

   Jael was honored. _____

   Sisera's mother's distress was described. _____

   God was once again honored. _____

2. The theme throughout Judges 4–5 is courage and honor—the courage to obey God's call and the honor that it brings. Tell how each of the following lacked courage and honor.

   Barak _____

   Sisera _____

   Tribe of Reuben _____

   The people of Gilead _____

   Tribe of Dan _____

   Tribe of Asher _____

3. Tell how each of the following were courageous and gained honor because of it.

   Deborah _____

   Jael _____

   Barak _____

   Tribe of Ephraim _____

   Tribe of Benjamin _____

   Tribe of Zebulun _____

   Tribe of Issachar _____

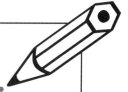

Another Cry to the Lord

▶ A New Judge

When the Israelites cried to the Lord because of the Midianites, God raised up another judge. Gideon was hiding in the mountains like the rest of the Israelites. Read Judges 6:7–32 to find out more about this unlikely choice for a judge.

Read each statement below and decide if it is true or false. Correct the false statements to make them true.

1. The angel of the Lord came and sat down under an oak tree.

   _____

2. Gideon was squeezing grapes in a winepress.

   _____

3. An angel told Gideon that God was with him.

   _____

4. Gideon said that the Lord had blessed Israel.

   _____

5. God called Gideon to save Israel.

   _____

6. Gideon said that he was from the most powerful clan.

   _____

7. Gideon prepared a meal to receive a sign from the angel.

   _____

8. When fire consumed the meal, it became clear to Gideon that the Lord was speaking to him.

   _____

9. God told Gideon to destroy the idols throughout all of Israel.

   _____

10. Fearing the people's reaction, Gideon pulled down the Baal and the Asherah pole at night.

   _____

11. Gideon's father disowned him and said, "Let us defend Baal!"

   _____

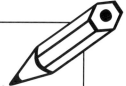

Another Cry to the Lord

▶The Weakest and the Least

When God looked for a judge to lead his people, he didn't look for things the world might think are important. This time God called a man who described himself as the least member of the weakest clan. God wanted to be sure that the world could see that the power and glory was his alone.

1. In what ways was Gideon unfit to lead God's people? _____

_____

_____

_____

2. How did God use Gideon to do important things? _____

_____

_____

3. In what ways might the world look at you as having not much power or importance?

_____

_____

_____

_____

_____

_____

4. How might God call you to do important things in his name?

_____

_____

_____

_____

_____

_____

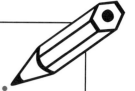

Gideon against Midian

▶**Gideon's Army**

Gideon gathered all of the men he could to attack the Midianites. But God had different plans. This was going to be his battle, not Israel's. Read Judges 7:1–8, and answer the following questions.

1. What was the size of Gideon's original army? _____

2. What was the size of Gideon's second army? _____

3. What was the size of the actual fighting army? _____

4. Why do you think God used so few soldiers? _____

_____

▶**The Midianite's Nightmare**

God sent Gideon up to the Midianite camp just in time for him to overhear one of the soldiers describe his dream. The Midianite's nightmare would prove to be a dream come true for Gideon. Read Judges 7:9–15, and answer the following questions.

5. How many Midianites and other eastern peoples were in the valley? _____

_____

6. Describe the Midianite's dream. _____

_____

7. How did the Midianite's friend interpret his dream? _____

_____

▶**Trumpets, Lights, Action!**

Gideon was facing depressing odds. His army had been reduced to a mere handful of men. They had only a few inferior weapons compared to those of their enemies. But a few men, a sound military strategy, and some unusual tools were all that God needed for victory. Read Judges 7:16–25, and answer the following questions.

8. What "tools" did Gideon's men use in addition to their swords? _____

_____

9. Describe how Gideon routed the Midianite camp. _____

_____

_____

10. Who helped Gideon by capturing two Midianite leaders? _____

Gideon against Midian

▶**The Bloody Brother**

Gideon turned down the chance to be king, but Abimelech didn't follow his example. He used his brothers to gain popularity and to make the people fear him. Read Judges 9:1–6 for answers to the following questions.

1. Where did Abimelech get money to hire followers? _____

   _____

2. Who were Abimelech's followers? _____

3. What did Abimelech do to his brothers? _____

▶**Jotham's Fable**

Gideon's youngest son, Jotham, escaped Abimelech's murder spree. Before he fled for good, however, he shouted down to the citizens of Shechem, telling them a story. It was a fable that compares men to trees. Read Judges 9:7–21 for answers to the following questions.

4. What trees turned down the chance to be king? _____

   _____

5. Why weren't the trees interested in being king? _____

   _____

6. The thornbush was a scraggly plant that produced nothing of value. It caused farmers a lot of

   trouble. What did this metaphor say about Abimelech? _____

   _____

▶**Abimelech Repaid**

Abimelech reigned as king for three years. The fickle citizens of Shechem later turned against him. He and his band of outlaws managed to defeated the Shechemites and destroyed their city. The refugees fled to a nearby pagan temple; Abimelech followed them and burned the refugees alive in the temple. Then he attacked another city named Thebez, whose citizens hid in the city tower. Read Judges 9:50–56 for answers to the following questions.

7. How did Abimelech die? _____

8. How were Gideon and Abimelech opposites? _____

   _____

   _____

   _____

Deliverance by an Outcast

Each generation of Israelites seemed to be less God-fearing than the generation before. Read Judges 10–11, and then fill in the blanks to describe the events. Answers may be more than one word.

1. Tola, a man of the tribe of _____, led Israel 23 years. (10:1–2)

2. Jair judged Israel 22 years. Evidently he was wealthy because he had

   _____ sons, who rode _____ donkeys and controlled

   _____ towns. (10:3–4)

3. When Israel cried out to God he told them to _____.

   (10:10–14)

4. The Israelites got rid of the foreign gods, and they _____. (10:15–16)

5. Israel's new judge, Jephthah, was considered an outcast by his _____. (11:1–2)

6. The elders of Gilead promised Jephthah that _____ if he

   would be their commander in the fight against the Ammonites. (11:8)

7. The king of the Ammonites wanted _____. (11:13)

8. Jephthah responded by telling Ammon's king that Israel _____.

   (11:14–15)

9. The Lord gave Jephthah _____ over the Ammonites. (11:32–33)

10. Jephthah's rash vow cost him _____. (11:30–31, 34–39)

11. Jephthah is listed as a man of _____ in Hebrews 11:32–33.

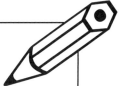

Samson: God's Renegade

▶ **Samson IQ Test**

Use this quiz to see how many details you remember about Samson.

1. When did Samson's parents first know that he was special? _____
_____

2. Samson could not have any wine, grape, or fermented drink; he could not cut his hair or have any contact with dead bodies. What was the name for a person who observed these restrictions?
_____

3. Samson wanted to marry a woman in Timnah, Philistia. What happened to Samson on his way to visit her? _____
_____

4. At the wedding feast, Samson told a riddle that no one could solve. What was the riddle about?
_____

5. The riddle was solved, and Samson had to pay up. How was the riddle solved, and how did Samson pay his guests? _____
_____

6. What happened to Samson's wife? _____

7. What did Samson do when he found out that his wife was no longer his? _____
_____

8. How did the Philistines react? _____

9. To get even, Samson killed many more Philistines. The Philistines, in turn, set up camp in Judah. They wanted Samson, so the men of Judah went to Samson. What did the men of Judah want to do? _____
_____

10. What promise did Samson want from the men of Judah? _____
_____

11. What happened when the men of Judah turned Samson over to the Philistines? _____
_____

12. What did Samson ask God for after he killed the Philistines? _____

13. How many years did Samson lead Israel? _____

Unit 8, Lesson 7/1

Samson: God's Renegade

▶**Judges 13**

1. What tribe was Samson's family from? _____

2. What did the angel tell Manoah's wife about the son she would have? _____
   _____

3. What was Manoah's prayer? _____
   _____

4. What amazing thing happened when Manoah prepared a burnt offering? _____
   _____

5. What Manoah's reaction? his wife's? _____
   _____
   _____
   _____

6. What happened to Samson as he grew? _____

▶**Judges 14**

1. What was the background of Samson's wife? _____

2. What happened to Samson on the way to Timnah? _____
   _____

3. What did Samson find when he passed by the lion carcass later? _____
   _____

4. What riddle did Samson tell his wedding guests? _____
   _____

5. Why did Samson say, "If you had not plowed with my heifer, you would not have solved my riddle"? _____
   _____

6. How did Samson pay off his debt? _____
   _____

7. What happened to Samson's wife? _____

Unit 8, Lesson 7/2

Judges 15

1. What gift did Samson bring to his wife? _____

2. What offer did Samson's father-in-law make when Samson returned? _____
    _____
    _____

3. What did Samson do to get even? _____
    _____

4. How did the Philistines respond to Samson's fire? _____

5. What did Samson do? _____

6. How did the Philistines react? _____

7. How many men went to Samson? What did they want to do?_____
    _____

8. What happened when the Philistines saw Samson? _____

9. After Samson broke his ropes, what did he find? What did he do with it? _____
    _____

10. How did God provide for Samson after his victory? _____

Strong in Flesh—Weak in Spirit

Samson repeatedly failed to respect God and his Nazirite vows. In the end Samson's irreverence went too far. After toying with Delilah and her tricks several times, he seemed to think that nothing could stop him. He forgot the true source of his strength. Read the Bible verses indicated, and answer the questions below.

Judges 16:4–20—Samson and Delilah

1. Why was it foolish for Samson to pursue Philistine women again? _____
   _____

2. Why did Delilah want to know the source of Samson's strength? _____
   _____
   _____

3. What were the three lies that Samson told Delilah about how to subdue him? _____
   _____
   _____

4. After Delilah shaved Samson's head, he thought that he could shake himself free. Why wasn't
   he able to do that? _____
   _____

Judges 16:21–31—Samson's Death

5. How did the Philistines hurt and humiliate Samson? _____
   _____

6. Why do you think the writer of Judges mentions that Samson's hair was returning? _____
   _____

7. Why did the Philistines gather in Dagon's temple? _____
   _____

8. Why did they bring Samson to the temple? _____
   _____

9. What was Samson really doing while the 3,000 men and women watched him stumble about?
   _____

10. How did God remember Samson just before his death? _____
    _____

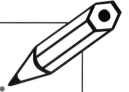

When All Did as They Saw Fit

▶**The Breakdown of Religion**

To help you understand the story you are about to study, open your student text to page 158. Read the section titled **Blessings and Curses**. Then read Judges 17 to find out how everyone did as they saw fit in their religious life. Fill in the blanks with the correct words from the passage.

1. An Ephraimite named _____ stole money from his mother.

2. After the mother got the money back, she dedicated it to the _____ in a strange way.

3. She asked her son to use the silver to make _____.

4. Micah made a _____ for his idols.

5. He appointed his own son to serve as his _____.

6. Later Micah hired a young _____ to be his very own priest.

7. Micah thought that the _____ would be good to him now.

▶   Read **Danites on the Move** (page 159) in your student text. Then read Judges 18 to learn how the tribe of Danites also did whatever they wanted and called it God's will.

1. Describe how the Danites' treated Micah. _____

    _____

    _____

2. Describe the Danites' treatment of the peaceful town of Laish. _____

    _____

The Breakdown of Society

The next story is filled with sin and violence. Read Judges 19. To help you further understand what some of the people in the story were thinking, read **Concubines** and **This Man Is My Guest** (page 160) in your student text. Then complete each of these statements.

1. When the Levite _____, her father gladly welcomed him, since their separation had brought the family disgrace.

2. Uncomfortable with the idea of _____ because the inhabitants were heathens, the Levite and his concubine moved on to Gibeah in Benjamin.

3. They were about to _____ because no one took them into their homes.

4. An old man _____. He was probably afraid that they wouldn't be safe in the square during the night.

5. The wicked Benjamite men wanted the owner of the house to _____, but the Levite's concubine was forced to go to them instead.

6. When the Levite _____, he found his concubine lying at the doorstep, dead.

7. The Levite _____ and sent the pieces to all parts of Israel so that they would realize how great was the sin in the land.

Read **Hardly a Sling Shooter Left** (page 160) in your student text.

Judges 21:25 describes these times as days when "everyone did as he saw fit." Write down as many examples as you can from the story of the Levite's concubine and the defeat of the tribe of Benjamin.

_____

_____

_____

_____

_____

Name _____

A Hebrew Short Story

Complete each section as you read through the Book of Ruth.

	Setting	Characters	Action
Introduction: Ruth 1:1–5			
Scene 1: Ruth 1:6–22			
Scene 2: Ruth 2:1–23			

197

	Setting	Characters	Action
▼ Scene 3: Ruth 3:1-18			
▼ Scene 4: Ruth 4:1-12			
▼ Conclusion: Ruth 4:13-22			

Name _____

Promise Made—Promise Kept

▶ Answer the following questions about 1 Samuel 1–2.

1. Why was Elkanah's wife Peninnah unkind to his other wife, Hannah? _____
   _____

2. Why was Hannah praying in the temple? What did she promise God if he granted her request?
   _____

3. Who were Eli's sons? _____

4. How did they anger God? _____
   _____

5. What did a prophet of God tell Eli would happen to his sons and his family as a result of their
   disobedience? _____
   _____

6. What did Hannah bring to Samuel when she came to visit him each year? _____

7. How did God bless Hannah for presenting Samuel to God? _____
   _____

8. Look up 1 Samuel 2:26 and Luke 2:52. What do you notice about the descriptions of Samuel
   and Jesus? _____
   _____

9. What does this comparison tell you? _____
   _____
   _____

10. How can you grow in the favor of God? _____
    _____

Promise Made—Promise Kept

Samuel's mother, Hannah, and Jesus' mother, Mary, both responded to the gift of a child by praising God through prayer. Compare their prayers.

	Hannah's Prayer (1 Samuel 2:1–10)	Mary's Prayer (Luke 1:46–55)
1. How does each mother begin her prayer?		
2. Whom does each woman say the Lord brought low or defeated?		
3. Who does the Lord lift up (raise) or exalt, guard, or strengthen?		
4. As she ends her prayer, what does each woman say God will do?		

Write a prayer like those of Hannah and Mary. Start by praising God. Then write three or four comparisons of how God will bring low those who are not faithful to his commands and raise those who are. Complete your prayer by seeking God's blessing on those whom he has chosen and loves. Use vivid images and descriptions like the prayers of the two mothers.

Judgment on Israel

▶ **Here I Am, Lord**

Narrator 1: Early in the morning, while Samuel was still asleep, God called to him.

Narrator 2: Samuel called out,

Samuel: "Here I am."

Narrator 2: And he ran to Eli and said,

Samuel: "Here I am; you called me."

Narrator 3: Eli, still half asleep, responded to Samuel by saying,

Eli: "I did not call; go back and lie down."

Narrator 4: Samuel listened to the priest and went back to bed.

Narrator 2: A short time later God called to Samuel again.

Narrator 1: Again Samuel thought that Eli was calling him. He went to Eli and said,

Samuel: "Here I am; you called me."

Eli: "My son, I did not call; go back and lie down."

Narrator 4: Samuel did not recognize that God was speaking to him.

Narrator 3: The Lord called to Samuel a third time, and Samuel once again got up and went to Eli.

Samuel: "Here I am; you called me."

Narrator 2: Eli finally realized that it was God who was calling Samuel. He told Samuel,

Eli: "Go and lie down, and if he calls you, say, 'Speak, Lord, for your servant is listening.'"

Narrator 3: So Samuel went back to bed.

Narrator 1: The Lord came and stood there, calling to Samuel as he had before.

God's Voice: "Samuel! Samuel!"

Samuel: "Speak, Lord, for your servant is listening."

God's Voice: "I am about to do something in Israel that will make the ears of everyone who hears it tingle. I will carry out my judgment against Eli's family. I told him that I would judge his family forever because of the sin he knew about. He failed to discipline his sons, and now his family will be punished forever."

Narrator 4: Samuel slept until morning, and then he opened the doors of the temple.

Narrator 2: He was afraid to tell Eli what God had said to him.

Narrator 3: Eli called to Samuel, and Samuel answered,

Samuel: "Here I am."

Eli: "What did the Lord say to you? Don't hide it from me."

Narrator 1: Samuel told Eli everything, hiding nothing from him. Eli responded by saying,

Eli: "He is the Lord; let him do what is good in his eyes."

Narrator 4: The Lord was with Samuel as he grew up, and the Lord continued to appear at Shiloh, revealing himself to Samuel through his word.

Unit 9, Lesson 2/1

Judgment on Israel

▶ Answer the following questions after reading 1 Samuel 4.

1. How many Israelite men did the Philistines kill at the battle described in verse 2? _____
   _____

2. What plan did the Israelites have to assure a victory the next time they fought the Philistine army?
   _____

3. Who came and stood by the ark of the covenant? _____

4. How did the Israelite camp respond when they saw the ark? _____
   _____

5. How did the Philistines respond when they heard that the Israelites had the ark in camp?
   _____
   _____

6. How great was Israel's defeat in the battle? _____
   _____

7. What happened when Eli heard the news of Israel's horrible losses? _____
   _____

8. What was the name of Eli's grandson that was born on that day? Why was that name chosen?
   _____
   _____

Name _____

Battle of the Gods

Trace the route that the ark of the covenant took, starting at Shiloh and arriving again in Israel. Look up the verse or verses in Judges 4–5 for each town. Then write what happened to the ark and the people in that town.

Shiloh (1 Samuel 4:3–4)

Kiriath Jearim (1 Samuel 6:21—7:2)

Beth Shemesh (1 Samuel 6:13–20)

North

Jabbok

Jordan

Dead Sea

Shiloh

Kiriath Jearim
Jerusalem

Aphek

Ashdod

Ekron Beth
Shemesh

Gath

Great Sea

Aphek (1 Samuel 4:1, 11)

Ashdod (1 Samuel 5:2–8)

Ekron (1 Samuel 5:10–12)

Gath (1 Samuel 5:8–10)

Name _____

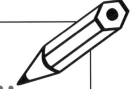

But Everybody Has One

Read 1 Samuel 8, and then complete the following questions.

1. List the three reasons that Israel wanted a king. _____
_____

2. What advice did God give to Samuel when he heard Israel's request for a king? _____
_____

3. Deuteronomy 17:14–20 lists God's commands for Israel and its future king. List at least five of
God's commands for a king. _____
_____
_____
_____
_____

4. What are four things Samuel warns the people that their king will do? _____
_____
_____
_____
_____

5. What differences do you notice about the qualities of a king that Deuteronomy lists and those
that Samuel lists? _____
_____

6. What do you think that the leaders of today's nations put their trust in? _____
_____

7. List five qualities that you think a good king should possess. _____
_____

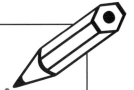

Saul—Israel's First Nagid

▶ Read 1 Samuel 9–10, and answer the following questions.

1. How is Saul described at the beginning of 1 Samuel 9? _____
_____

2. What was Saul searching for? _____

3. What had Samuel been told before Saul arrived? _____
_____

4. What did Saul tell Samuel about his family? _____
_____

5. How did Samuel show the people at the feast that Saul was important? (1 Samuel 9:23–24)
_____

6. How did Saul spend the night? _____

7. After Samuel anointed Saul privately, Samuel told Saul that God would send him three signs to confirm that he was God's anointed. What were the three signs? _____
_____
_____
_____
_____
_____

8. What does 1 Samuel 10:9 say happened to Saul? _____
_____

9. When people who knew Saul heard him prophesy, how did they react? _____
_____

10. What did Saul fail to tell his uncle? _____
_____

11. Where was Saul when Samuel announced at Mizpah that he would be king? _____
_____

12. How did the Israelites react when they met their new king? _____
_____

Saul's First Battle

As Saul began his reign, he showed potential to be a godly king for Israel. Look up the Bible reference for each positive characteristic listed. Write down how Saul showed that he was a man of God.

1. **Humble** 1 Samuel 9:21; 10:22	
2. **Restrained** 1 Samuel 10:27; 11:13	
3. **Concerned for Israel** 1 Samuel 11:1–8	
4. **Wise** 1 Samuel 11:9–11	
5. **Honored God** 1 Samuel 11:15	
6. **Filled with God's Spirit** 1 Samuel 10:9–10; 11:6–11	

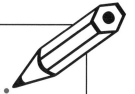

Covenant Renewal

▶ Read 1 Samuel 12, and then answer the following questions.

1. What things did Samuel say that he had never done to God's people? (1 Samuel 12:3–5)

   _____

2. What did Samuel use for evidence of God's faithfulness? _____

   _____

   _____

3. What miracle did God perform to lead Israel to repentance? _____

   _____

4. What did the people ask Samuel to do when they witnessed the miracle? _____

   _____

   _____

5. What did the Israelites need to do to turn to God? _____

   _____

6. Why wouldn't God reject them? _____

   _____

7. What did Samuel promise to do for them? _____

   _____

8. What final warning did Samuel give the people of Israel? _____

   _____

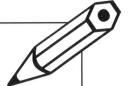

Saul's Lack of Trust

▶ Read 1 Samuel 13:1–15, and then answer the following questions.

1. Why did the people gather again at Gilgal? _____

_____

2. How did the Israelites respond to the Philistine army? _____

_____

3. Why did Saul wait seven days at Gilgal? _____

_____

4. Why did Saul offer the sacrifice? _____

_____

5. Why was it wrong for Saul to offer the sacrifice? _____

_____

6. What excuses did Saul give Samuel for his sin of disobedience? _____

_____

7. What was Saul's punishment for thinking that he could act as God's priest? _____

_____

8. Why do you think God punished Saul so severely? _____

_____

To Obey Is Better Than Sacrifice

▶ Answer the following questions based on 1 Samuel 14–16.

1. How did Saul's son Jonathan show his trust in God when he and his armor-bearer attacked the Philistines? (1 Samuel 14:6–14) _____

   _____

   _____

2. Following Jonathan's attack, what did God do to deliver the Philistines to the Israelites? (1 Samuel 14:15) _____

   _____

3. What rash oath did Saul make the day of the battle? _____

   _____

4. Who unknowingly broke the oath? _____

5. What did he eat? _____

6. What did he think of Saul's oath? (1 Samuel 14:29–30) _____

   _____

   _____

7. Why wasn't Jonathan killed for breaking the oath? (1 Samuel 14:45) _____

   _____

8. Whom did Samuel command Saul to completely destroy? (1 Samuel 15:2–3) _____

   _____

9. How did Saul disobey God when he attacked these people? _____

   _____

10. What excuse did Saul give Samuel? _____

    _____

11. What was the result of Saul's disobedience? _____

12. Copy 1 Samuel 15:22b. What did this verse say to Saul, and what does it mean to you?

    _____

    _____

    _____

    _____

13. What was Samuel's relationship with Saul after this event? _____

_____

14. God asked Samuel to go to Bethlehem to anoint a new leader, but Samuel was afraid. Why was

Samuel afraid, and what excuse did God give him? (1 Samuel 16:2–3) _____

_____

_____

15. Why did Samuel first think Eliab would be the next king? _____

_____

16. Copy 1 Samuel 16:7b. What did this verse say to Samuel and what does it mean to you?

_____

_____

_____

_____

_____

17. Why did David seem to be the unlikely son to anoint? _____

_____

18. Who knew that David had been anointed as king? _____

19. What showed that God had rejected Saul? _____

20. Why was David called to serve King Saul? _____

_____

21. How did God use David's time with Saul to prepare him to be king? _____

_____

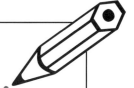

To Obey Is Better Than Sacrifice

As Saul continued his reign over Israel, he showed that he was no longer a godly king. Look up the Bible references for each negative characteristic listed below. Write down how Saul showed that he was no longer the man of God's choosing.

1. **Impatient** 1 Samuel 13:8–10	
2. **Disobedient** 1 Samuel 13:8–10; 15:7–9	
3. **Hasty in Speech** 1 Samuel 14:24; 44–45	
4. **Blamed Others** 1 Samuel 13:11–12; 15:15	
5. **Honored Self** 1 Samuel 13:12; 15:12	
6. **Lacked God's Spirit** 1 Samuel 16:14	

Name _____

Taking Up the Challenge

Use 1 Samuel 17 to help you fill in the blanks.

The armies of the _____ and Philistines were gathered on two hills. The Philistine army had a champion named _____. He was over _____ tall and wore a bronze helmet on his head. He wore a coat of armor that weighed _____. His weapons included a javelin and a spear. A _____ went ahead of him into battle.

Each day Goliath stood and shouted at the _____. He wanted them to choose a man to fight him. If the _____ won, the Philistines would serve them. If the Philistines won, the _____ would become their servants. Each day that they heard the Philistine's words, _____ were afraid.

David was sent by his father _____ to bring _____ to his brothers and bring back word from the camp. As David talked with his brothers on the battle line, _____ approached, shouting insults at the Israelites. Seeing the giant, the Israelites _____.

Saul promised that the man who defeated the Philistine champion would receive _____, marry _____, and that his family would not have to pay _____. Saul heard David talk about the giant and called him to his tent. Saul did not think David could fight the Philistine's champion, because he was only a _____. David told the king that _____ helped him kill both a _____ and a _____ while he was watching his father's sheep. Saul allowed David to fight the Philistine, but he wanted David to wear his _____. David refused.

As David approached Goliath, he chose _____ from a stream and put them in his bag. Goliath saw David approach and insulted him. He asked if David thought he was a _____ that he approached him with _____. David told the giant that he came to him in the name of _____. David took out one of his _____ and slung it, striking the Philistine on the _____, killing him. By trusting in _____, David won the victory for Israel.

Name _____

Tens of Thousands

▶ Fill out the chart based on selected passages from 1 Samuel 18.

	Saul's Attempt to Kill David	God's Blessing on David
Verse 10–11		
Verses 12–16		
Verses 24–27		
Verses 28–30		

▶ Turn to Psalm 59, which David wrote when Saul was attempting to kill him. Fill out the chart below.

	Description of the Enemy	Description of God's Protection
Verses 2–5		
Verses 6–9		
Verses 12–13		
Verses 14–17		

David and Jonathan

▶ A cinquain is a five-line poem that follows a specific pattern. On cinquain form is:

    Line 1: two syllables

    Line 2: four syllables

    Line 3: six syllables

    Line 4: eight syllables

    Line 5: two syllables

David and Jonathan had a close friendship. Write a cinquain that describes the friendship of David and Jonathan.

_____

_____

_____

_____

_____

▶ Another form for a cinquain poem is:

    Line 1: a noun

    Line 2: two adjectives describing line 1

    Line 3: three verbs related to line 1

    Line 4: a four word phrase about line 1

    Line 5: a noun that renames line 1

Use this form to write another poem about David, Jonathan, or Saul.

_____

_____

_____

_____

_____

Name _____

David, the Fugitive

David stayed in several different towns and areas as he hid from King Saul. Use the numbered boxes below and the verses from 1 Samuel 21–23 to locate David. Draw a line from the box to the area or city. Then write down what happened to David in that location, paying special attention to how God protected David wherever he was.

① 1 Samuel 21:1-9

② 1 Samuel 21:10-14

③ 1 Samuel 22:1-2

④ 1 Samuel 22:3-4

⑤ 1 Samuel 22:5, 20-23

⑥ 1 Samuel 23:1-12

⑦ 1 Samuel 23:14-23

⑧ 1 Samuel 23:24-28

⑨ 1 Samuel 23:29

Great Sea

Jordan

Dead Sea

Nob ●
Jerusalem ●

En Gedi ●

DESERT OF ZIPH

DESERT OF MAON

● Mizpah

Gath ●

Adullam ●

Keilah ●

FOREST OF HERETH

Name _____

Insult and Revenge

▸ Read 1 Samuel 25, and then answer the following questions.

1. While in the Desert of Maon, David sent ten men to a Calebite named Nabal with a request. What was the request? _____

2. How did Nabal respond to David's request? _____
_____

3. What was David's reaction when his men returned with Nabal's response? _____
_____

4. When one of Nabal's servants told Abigail how her husband had responded to David's men, what did she do? _____
_____
_____

5. What was David's response to Abigail? _____
_____

6. When Abigail returned home, what was Nabal doing? _____
_____

7. What happened when Abigail told Nabal what she had done? _____
_____

8. What did David ask Abigail after he heard of Nabal's death? _____
_____

▸ Read Proverbs 15:1–14. Many of these verses apply to today's lesson. Choose three verses or partial verses that apply to this story, and write them down. After each verse, explain how it applies to David, Nabal, or Abigail.

_____
_____
_____
_____
_____
_____
_____

A Robe, a Spear, and a Jug

Saul was chasing David all over Israel. Saul almost cornered David and his men in a cave, and David could have killed Saul. Read 1 Samuel 24 and 26 to find out what happened, and then fill in the chart below.

Chapter	How David Catches Saul Unaware	The Advice of David's Men	The Object Taken	Saul's Response	David's Response
1 Samuel 24					
1 Samuel 26					

Singing on the Run

- Write the name of your assigned psalm at the top to the page. Answer the following questions about your psalm.

Psalm _____

1. Read the description of your psalm, found just before the first verse. Write down the circumstances in David's life surrounding your psalm. _____

   _____

   _____

   _____

   _____

   _____

   _____

2. What does David ask God to do in this psalm? _____

   _____

   _____

3. For what does David praise God? _____

   _____

   _____

4. Write down two concrete or vivid images that David used in your psalm. Write down the verse in which each appears. _____

   _____

5. Write down the first verse and the last verse of your psalm. How are these two verse alike? How do they act as bookends for the psalm? _____

   _____

   _____

6. Turn to page 197 in your student text to the explanation of parallel structure in the psalms. Write down an example of similar, contrasting, or completing parallelism in your psalm. Explain what type of parallelism the psalmist used. _____

   _____

   _____

Write a psalm of deliverance. Think of times that God has protected you from sickness or injury. Maybe God has led you or your family though some painful experiences. You may want to create a psalm asking God to deliver you from future harm or temptation. Use vivid images and two different examples of parallelism. Make sure that your first verse and your last verse tie your psalm together.

_____

_____

_____

_____

_____

_____

_____

_____

_____

_____

_____

_____

_____

_____

_____

_____

_____

David among the Philistines

▶ **Running to Philistia—1 Samuel 27**

1. Where did David and his men go to escape King Saul? _____
   _____

2. Who went along with David when he escaped King Saul? _____
   _____

3. King Achish gave David and his men the city of Ziklag. While they were living there, they raid-
   ed villages of both Israel's and Philistia's enemies. What did Achish think David was doing?
   _____

4. How did David make sure that the king never knew what villages he was really attacking?
   _____
   _____

5. What did King Achish believe that the people of Israel thought about David? _____
   _____
   _____

▶ **Marching with King Achish—1 Samuel 28:1–3 and 1 Samuel 29**

1. What position did King Achish ask David to take? _____
   _____

2. Where were David and his men positioned when they marched with King Achish? _____

3. Why didn't the Philistines want David to fight with them? _____
   _____
   _____

4. What words did Achish use to describe David? _____
   _____

5. Where did David go after he left King Achish? _____
   _____

The Raiding Amalekites—1 Samuel 30

1. When David and his men returned home, what did they find? _____
   _____
   _____

2. In their anger the men blamed David. What did they threaten to do? _____
   _____

3. David asked Abiathar, the high priest, what he should do. What did God tell David? _____
   _____
   _____

4. David won a quick victory, killing many Amalekites. What did David recover when the battle was
   over? _____
   _____
   _____

5. Why did David send some of the plunder to the elders of Judah? _____
   _____
   _____

Cut off from God

Behind the true statements write down the chapter and verse or verses that prove that the statement is correct. Correct false statements to make them true, and again include the chapter and verse or verses.

A Desperate Act—1 Samuel 28:3–24

1. Saul disobeyed God and kept all of the mediums and witches in the kingdom of Israel to help him know the future throughout his reign. _____

   _____

2. Saul was terrified of the Philistine army. He asked God what he should do, but God refused to answer. _____

   _____

3. Saul disguised himself and went to the Witch of Endor. _____

   _____

4. The witch was happy to see Saul and welcomed his business. _____

   _____

5. Samuel told Saul that he would have a huge victory over the Philistines that day.

   _____

   _____

Saul's Reign Ends—1 Samuel 31

1. Saul's three sons were killed in battle before Saul died. _____

   _____

2. Saul did not want to be killed by Philistines, so he asked his armor-bearer to kill him. The armor-bearer killed Saul. _____

   _____

3. The Philistines had a great victory over the Israelites. The Philistines occupied many of the Israelite cities. _____

   _____

4. The Philistines returned to the battle site and stripped the dead. They cut off the heads of Saul and his sons and displayed them throughout Philistia. The bodies of the men were displayed on the city walls of Beth Shan. _____

   _____

5. Israelite men from Jabesh Gilead rescued the bodies from the Philistines. Then they displayed the bodies of Saul and his sons on their own city gates. _____

_____

▶ **David Mourns—2 Samuel 1:1–15**

1. David heard the news of Saul's death when he was on the way back to Ziklag.

_____

_____

2. The young man who told David about the deaths of Saul and his sons was from the tribe of Benjamin. _____

_____

3. The messenger told David that King Saul was fatally wounded when he found him and that Saul asked the messenger to kill him before the Philistines arrived. The messenger said that he had killed Saul and then took his crown and arm band to David.

_____

_____

4. David and his men were sad when they heard of King's Saul's death. They tore their clothes, mourned, wept, and fasted to show their grief. _____

_____

5. David rewarded the messenger for bringing him the king's crown and arm band.

_____

_____

Under David and Solomon

Each lesson will be assigned a one-word summary. In the space provided, write how the word summarizes the lesson. If you think of a better word to summarize the lesson, cross out the one provided, fill in your own, and write your explanation.

Lesson	Summary	Explanation
1. David, King of Judah	Tribe	
2. David, King of Israel	Capital	
3. God's Promise to David	Covenant	
4. David's Victories	Leaders	
5. David's Kindness	Promise	

Lesson	Summary	Explanation
6. A Broken David	Coward	
7. Like Father, Like Son	Discipline	
8. Son versus Father	Appearance	
9. Hushai and Ahithophel Give Advice	Loyalty	
10. The Journey Back	Humble	
11. God's Justice and Mercy	Mercy	

Lesson	Summary	Explanation
12. Songs from David's Life	Response	
13. God Chooses His Own Man	Crown	
14. David's Death	Peace	
15. Solomon's Wisdom	Unity	
16. The Proverbs: Knowing Right from Wrong	Wisdom	
17. Solomon's Temple	Construction	
18. The Dedication	Glory	

David, King of Judah

Answer the following questions based on 2 Samuel 2–4.

▶Anointing in Hebron—2 Samuel 2:1–7

1. What happened to David at Hebron? _____

2. What message did David send to the men of Jabesh Gilead? _____

_____

▶David's House or Saul's House?—2 Samuel 2:8–32

3. Who led Ish-Bosheth's army, and who led David's army? _____

_____

4. Who was Asahel, and how did he die? _____

_____

5. Why did the two sides quit fighting on the day Asahel was killed? _____

_____

▶Abner Changes Sides—2 Samuel 3–4

6. What did David demand before he would make an agreement with Abner? _____

_____

7. Whom did Abner speak with before he spoke to David? What did these people tell him?

_____

_____

8. How was Abner murdered? _____

_____

_____

9. How did David treat Abner's death? _____

_____

_____

10. How was Ish-Bosheth killed? _____

11. How did David treat the men who killed Ish-Bosheth? _____

_____

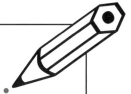

Name _____

David, King of Israel

▶ Answer the following questions based on 2 Samuel 5–6.

1. List three reasons that Israel recognized David as king.

_____

_____

_____

2. List three things that King Hiram sent David to help him build a palace in Jerusalem. _____

_____

3. List and write out four verses from 2 Samuel 5 that illustrate how David depended on God when he attacked the Philistines.

_____

_____

_____

_____

_____

_____

_____

_____

_____

_____

4. List three things that David did differently when he took the ark of the covenant to Jerusalem the second time. _____

_____

5. Look up Psalm 98. List at least three ways that the people were to make music to the Lord.

_____

God's Promise to David

David wanted to build a beautiful home where God's ark of the covenant could dwell. Instead God told David that he would build David a kingdom that would endure. Read 2 Samuel 7:5–17. In the large windows and door of the house below, write the promises that God made to David.

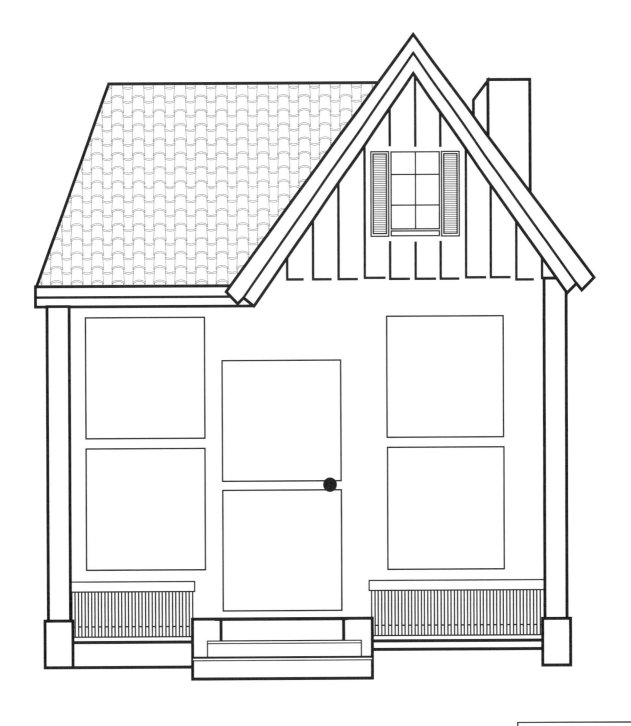

David's Victories

▶ Setting Up a Government

Fill in the chart describing David's government structure.

	Mighty Men	Levites	Scribes
Names of the Leaders	2 Samuel 8:16–18	2 Samuel 8:16–18	2 Samuel 8:16–18
Their Duties	1 Chronicles 11:10–25	1 Chronicles 23:1–6	2 Samuel 8:16–18; 1 Chronicles 27:32–34
How do you think they helped David and the Israelites?			

Name _____

David's Kindness

David made many promises and treaties throughout his life. Two of these are discussed in 2 Samuel 9 and 10. Read the chapter listed, and then fill in the chart.

Chapter	Whom did David make a promise to or treaty with?	How did he try to keep the promise?	How were David's good intentions interpreted?	What were the results of his actions?
2 Samuel 9				
2 Samuel 10				

A Broken David

Read 2 Samuel 11, and answer the following questions.

▶ The Setting and the Sin

1. Who was leading David's men into battle against the Ammonites? _____

2. Where was David while they were fighting? _____

3. Why do you think David wasn't with his troops? _____
   _____

4. When did David first see Bathsheba? _____
   _____

5. What did David know about her background before he asked her to come over? _____
   _____

6. After the affair, what news did Bathsheba send David? _____
   _____

▶ The Coverup

1. Why did David say that he was calling Uriah home from the army? _____
   _____

2. Why did David really want Uriah home? _____
   _____

3. Why did Uriah refuse to go home to his wife? _____
   _____
   _____

4. In frustration David sent Uriah back to the army with a message for Joab. What did that message say? _____
   _____

5. Why do you think David chose that method to get rid of Uriah? _____
   _____
   _____

6. How did David react when he heard the news of Uriah's death? _____
   _____
   _____

A Broken David

Psalm 51 has been divided into sections. Decide what you think would be the best title for each of the sections. When you have finished, go back over the psalm and apply it to the story of David and Bathsheba.

The Penitent's Psalm

_____

Have mercy on me, O God,
    according to your unfailing love;
according to your great compassion
    blot out my transgressions.
Wash away all my iniquity
    and cleanse me from my sin.

_____

For I know my transgressions,
    and my sin is always before me.
Against you, you only, have I sinned
    and done what is evil in your sight,
so that you are proved right when you speak
    and justified when you judge.
Surely I was sinful at birth,
    sinful from the time my mother conceived me.

_____

Surely you desire truth in the inner parts;
    you teach me wisdom in the inmost place.
Cleanse me with hyssop, and I will be clean;
    wash me, and I will be whiter than snow.
Let me hear joy and gladness;
    let the bones you have crushed rejoice.

Hide your face from my sins
    and blot out all my iniquity.
Create in me a pure heart, O God,
    and renew a steadfast spirit within me.
Do not cast me from your presence
    or take your Holy Spirit from me.
Restore to me the joy of your salvation
    and grant me a willing spirit, to sustain me.

Then I will teach transgressors your ways,
    and sinners will turn back to you.
Save me from bloodguilt, O God, the God who saves me,
    and my tongue will sing of your righteousness.

O Lord, open my lips,
    and my mouth will declare your praise.
You do not delight in sacrifice, or I would
    bring it;
    you do not take pleasure in burnt offerings.
The sacrifices of God are a broken spirit;
    a broken and contrite heart, O God, you will not despise.

In your good pleasure make Zion prosper;
    build up the walls of Jerusalem.
Then there will be righteous sacrifices,
    whole burnt offerings to delight you;
    then bulls will be offered on your altar.

How did David show that he wanted to restore fellowship with God?

_____

_____

_____

Like Father, Like Son

▶ **Amnon and Tamar**

1. After reading 2 Samuel 13:1–21, number the following events in the correct order.

_____ a. Tamar prepared food for Amnon.

_____ b. Amnon ordered Tamar to leave; she cried in vain. Amnon's "love" turned to hate.

_____ c. Absalom comforted and advised Tamar.

_____ d. Amnon burned with desire for Tamar.

_____ e. Jonadab gave Amnon advice on how to get Tamar alone.

_____ f. Amnon ordered Tamar to bed with him; she pleaded in vain.

_____ g. Tamar left crying.

_____ h. Amnon ordered his servants to leave so that he could be alone with Tamar.

_____ i. Absalom's anger burned against Amnon.

_____ j. Amnon ordered his servants to return and take Tamar out.

2. What do you think would be an appropriate punishment for David to give Amnon?

_____

_____

▶ **Amnon and Absalom**

3. After reading 2 Samuel 13:22–38, number the following events in the correct order.

_____ a. David was told that Absalom had killed all of the king's sons.

_____ b. David's other sons mounted their donkeys and fled from Absalom's party.

_____ c. Jonadab assured David that only his son Amnon was killed.

_____ d. David could not attend the festival and sent Amnon instead.

_____ e. Absalom asked his brothers to attend a sheep-shearing festival.

_____ f. David and his sons wept for Amnon's death.

_____ g. Amnon was killed by Absalom's men.

_____ h. David's watchman saw his sons returning from Absalom's party.

_____ i. Absalom fled to Geshur to live with his grandfather.

_____ j. Absalom ordered his men to kill Amnon at the festival.

4. What do you think would be an appropriate punishment for David to give Absalom?

_____

_____

Like Father, Like Son

Read 2 Samuel 14. In the boxes below, draw or write a description of what you think are the most important parts of the story.

Son versus Father

After reading 2 Samuel 15–16:14, complete the following chart. Not all of the people will have a relationship with both David and Absalom.

Person	Background Information	Relationship with David	Relationship with Absalom
Ittai			
Zadok			
Ahithophel			
Hushai			
Ziba			
Shimei			

Unit 10, Lesson 8

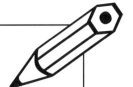

Hushai and Ahithophel Give Advice

▶ **Advising King Absalom**—2 Samuel 16:15—17:14

1. Why was Absalom suspicious of Hushai? _____
   _____

2. What did Ahithophel advise Absalom to do? _____
   _____

3. Why did he give Absalom this advice? _____
   _____

4. What prophecy did this fulfill? (2 Samuel 12:11–12) _____
   _____

5. What was Ahithophel's advice about fighting David? _____
   _____

6. What was Hushai's advice about fighting David? _____
   _____

7. Why did Absalom listen to Hushai's advice instead of Ahithophel's advice? _____
   _____

▶ **David Hears of the Advice**—2 Samuel 17:15–29

1. Whom did Hushai tell of Absalom's acceptance of his advice? _____
   _____

2. What did Hushai advise David to do? _____
   _____

3. What happened to delay the two men who were taking the message to David? _____
   _____
   _____

4. What did Ahithophel do when his advice was not taken? _____
   _____

5. Whom did Absalom place in charge of his army? _____
   _____

6. How did God provide for David and his family as they crossed the Jordan? _____
   _____

The Rebellion Ends—2 Samuel 18:1–18

1. Who led David's men in battle? _____

2. Why wouldn't they allow David to go into battle? _____

   _____

3. What did David do as the men left for battle? _____

   _____

4. What command concerning Absalom did David give his men? _____

   _____

5. How did Absalom meet his death? _____

   _____

6. How did the fighting end? _____

   _____

Mourning a Son—2 Samuel 18:19–19:8

1. Who wanted to bring the news of Absalom's death to David? _____

   _____

2. Who was asked to bring the advice instead? _____

3. Why do you think Joab chose the second man? _____

   _____

   _____

4. Who won the race to bring the news to David, and who told David of Absalom's death?

   _____

   _____

5. How did David react when he heard the news of Absalom's death? _____

   _____

6. What advice did Joab give David when he returned from the battle? _____

   _____

   _____

7. What did David do as a result of Joab's advice? _____

   _____

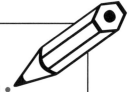

The Journey Back

▶ As a group, you are going to come up with questions about the readings that you think other groups should be able to answer. For each section of Scripture, think of three questions that can help others see the important ideas in that passage. Avoid details that will only stump others. Read the entire passage of Scripture before writing your questions.

▶**Crossing the Jordan**—2 Samuel 19:8b–39

Question 1 _____

_____

Question 2 _____

_____

Question 3 _____

_____

▶**Sheba's Rebellion**—2 Samuel 19:40—20:7

Question 1

_____

_____

Question 2

_____

_____

Question 3

_____

_____

▶**Joab Takes Charge**—2 Samuel 20:8–26

Question 1 _____

_____

Question 2 _____

_____

Question 3 _____

_____

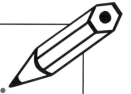

God's Justice and Mercy

After reading the assigned Scripture passages, indicate if the following statements are true or false. Rewrite all of the false statements to make them true.

▶ **Saul's Sin**—2 Samuel 21:1–14

1. God sent a famine to Israel as a result of an unpunished sin that Saul had committed during his reign. _____

_____

2. Israel was being punished because Saul had taken the idols of the Gibeonites and worshiped them. _____

_____

3. The Gibeonites said that they wanted seven of Saul's sons to be put to death as punishment for the crimes. _____

_____

4. David gave Mephibosheth and six of his brothers to the Gibeonites to kill.

_____

_____

5. After the deaths of the seven men, God blessed Israel with rain and listened to Israel's prayers.

_____

_____

▶ **David Counts**—2 Samuel 24:1–10

1. David received word from God that he should take a census.

_____

_____

2. Joab was eager to find out the number of fighting men in Israel.

_____

_____

3. It took Joab and his men over nine months to take the census.

_____

_____

4. Joab reported that there were 800,000 fighting men in Israel and 500,000 fighting men in Judah.

    _____

5. David arranged for a feast day in Israel to celebrate the blessing of many fighting men.

    _____

    _____

Israel Punished—2 Samuel 24:11–25

1. God told David of three possible punishments. David was to choose one punishment for Israel.

    _____

    _____

2. David agreed to have Israel punished by having God send a three-day plague.

    _____

    _____

3. The plague killed many people throughout Israel, but Jerusalem's losses were the greatest.

    _____

    _____

4. David bought a threshing floor and oxen to offer a sacrifice to God.

    _____

    _____

5. David built a new palace on the place where he gave an offering to God.

    _____

    _____

Songs from David's Life

After studying Psalm 43, write your own psalm of lament. Pattern your psalm after the example of David's psalms of lament.

Address—Write a call to the Lord.

_____

_____

_____

Complaint—Honestly complain to God; don't whine.

_____

_____

_____

Trust—Show your trust in God to answer you.

_____

_____

_____

Deliverance—Ask God to deliver you from your complaint.

_____

_____

_____

Assurance—Again express trust that God will answer you.

_____

_____

_____

Praise—Give thanks to God for all that he has done for you and will continue to do for you.

_____

_____

_____

_____

Name _____

Songs from David's Life

After studying Psalm 138, write your own psalm of thanksgiving. Pattern your psalm after the example of David's psalms of thanksgiving.

Introduction—Think of ways that God has helped you in the past.

_____

_____

_____

_____

Distress—Describe situations in which God has provided help.

_____

_____

_____

_____

Appeal—Write your cry of distress.

_____

_____

_____

_____

Deliverance—Describe God's deliverance from your difficult situations.

_____

_____

_____

_____

Testimony—Praise God for his mercy and faithfulness.

_____

_____

_____

_____

_____

Name _____

God Chooses His Own Man

▶ Read 1 Kings 1.

1. Put an A in the blank if the following people supported Adonijah. Put an S in the blank it they supported Solomon.

_____ a. Nathan

_____ b. Abiathar

_____ c. Benaiah

_____ d. Zadok

_____ e. Bathsheba

_____ f. Joab

_____ g. David

_____ h. Jonathan

2. What was the real purpose behind Adonijah's party? _____

_____

3. Adonijah invited all of his brothers to the party except Solomon. Why didn't he invite Solomon?

_____

4. Whom did Nathan the prophet tell of Adonijah's plans? _____

_____

5. What action did she take when she heard of Adonijah's plan?

_____

_____

6. What action did David take to obey God's plan for a future king for Israel? _____

_____

7. Why did everyone suddenly leave Adonijah's party? _____

_____

8. What did Adonijah do when he heard that Solomon had been made king?

_____

_____

9. What punishment did Solomon give Adonijah? _____

_____

David's Death

Read 1 Kings 2:1–12, 26–46, and then fill out the following chart. Not all of the squares will have answers.

	Crime against David and God	David's Advice for Punishment	Solomon's Orders	Replacement
Abiathar				
Joab				
Shimei				

Solomon's Wisdom

▶ Answer the following questions based on the Scripture passages given for each section.

▶ **A Wise Request**—1 Kings 3:1–15

1. Where did the Lord appear to Solomon? _____

2. How did God show his kindness to David? _____
   _____

3. What fears about being king did Solomon tell God? _____
   _____

4. What did Solomon ask God for? _____
   _____

5. Why do you think that this was a good request? _____
   _____
   _____

6. What did God promise Solomon along with wisdom? _____
   _____
   _____
   _____

▶ **A Wise Answer**—1 Kings 3:16–28

1. How had the child of one of the women died? _____
   _____

2. What did one woman claim that the other had done with the dead baby? _____
   _____

3. What did Solomon threaten to do with the baby? _____
   _____

4. What was the result of Solomon's decision? _____
   _____
   _____

5. Why was this decision important to the people of Israel? _____

_____

_____

▶ **Examples of Solomon's Wisdom**—1 Kings 4:29–34

1. What does the writer compare Solomon's wisdom to in verse 29? _____

_____

2. How many proverbs did Solomon write? _____

_____

3. What did Solomon teach about? _____

_____

4. Who came to hear Solomon speak? _____

_____

5. How do you think the fame of Solomon's wisdom helped God's people? _____

_____

_____

_____

The Proverbs: Knowing Right from Wrong

Contrasts

Many proverbs are only two lines long. They usually contrast opposite things or ideas. Read Proverbs 10. Write down four examples of items that are contrasted in the chapter.

1. _____
   _____

2. _____
   _____

3. _____
   _____

4. _____
   _____

Images

The Book of Proverbs is full of word pictures and images. Read Proverbs 25, and write down four verses that contain rich word pictures or images.

1. _____
   _____

2. _____
   _____

3. _____
   _____

4. _____
   _____

Similes

A simile is a word picture or image that is compared with something else using the words *like* or *as*. An example of this is Proverbs 25:25—"Like cold water to a weary soul is good news from a distant land." Read Proverbs 26, and list four examples of similes that you find in the chapter.

1. _____
   _____

2. _____

_____

3. _____

_____

4. _____

_____

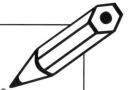

Solomon's Temple

1. Compare the size of the tabernacle to that of the temple by writing the temple's measurement in the chart below. Remember that a cubit equals 18".

	Tabernacle Exodus 36	Temple 1 Kings 7:2
Width	18'	
Length	45'	
Height	15'	

2. Identify some of the materials used to build the temple by reading the references from 1 Kings and filling in the names of the materials.

   • The roofing beams were made of _____. (6:9)

   • The interior was overlaid with pure _____. (6:20)

   • The cherubim were made of _____. (6:23)

   • The temple floors were laid with _____. (6:30)

   • The doors were made of _____. (6:23, 34)

   • The inner courtyard was built with _____ and

     _____. (6:36)

   • The throne hall and Hall of Justice were built of _____.(7:9)

   • Two pillars were built of _____. (7:15)

   • The ten lavers were made of _____. (7:27, 33)

   • All of the temple furniture was made of _____. (7:48–50)

3. Where did Solomon build the temple? (2 Chronicles 3:1–2) _____

   _____

4. How long did it take Solomon to build the temple? (1 Kings 6:38) _____

   _____

5. How long did it take Solomon to build his palace? (1 Kings 7:1) _____

6. Why do you think the Bible puts these two statements next to each other? _____

   _____

   _____

Solomon's Temple

1 Kings 6–7; 2 Chronicles 3–4

Label the following items and places in Solomon's temple on the diagram: portico, bronze altar, bronze sea, stands with basins, Jakin and Boaz pillars, side rooms, Holy Place, altar of incense, lampstands, tables for the bread of the Presence, Most Holy Place, and the ark. Use 1 Kings 6–7 and 2 Chronicles 3–4 as sources. If you really have trouble, turn to the pictures by 1 Kings 6–8 in *The NIV Study Bible* for help.

N

The Dedication

Turn to 1 Kings 8:22–52. Read the prayer of Solomon together as a group first. Then read it again, watching for examples of Solomon's thoughts about God, Solomon's prayers about God's people, and Solomon's requests for answered prayer. Write down your examples in the chart below.

Thoughts about God	Prayers about God's People	Requests for Answers

What can we learn from Solomon's prayer that can help improve our own prayer life? _____

_____

_____

_____

_____

_____

What Is Archaeology?

The first thing a biblical archaeologist would do is research. Some of the reference tools that a biblical archaeologist would use are the Bible and various Bible resources such as Bible dictionaries and encyclopedias. Use those reference tools to answer the following questions.

1. The following Bible passages come from stories you have covered in Bible class this year. What does each passage tell us about Ekron?

   a. Joshua 13:1–3 _____

   b. Joshua 15:1, 11, 20, 45 _____

   c. Judges 1:18 _____

   d. 1 Samuel 5:1, 6–7, 10 _____

   e. 1 Samuel 7:12–14 _____

   f. 1 Samuel 17:50–52 _____

   _____

2. Now look at the following Bible passages. These are from stories and passages you have not covered this year. Briefly write what each of these passages tells us about Ekron.

   a. 2 Kings 1:2–3 _____

   b. Amos 1:8 _____

   c. Zephaniah 2:4 _____

   d. Zechariah 9:5–7 _____

3. Use a Bible dictionary or concordance to find answers to the following questions.

   a. What god did people in Ekron worship? _____

   b. Who was in charge of Ekron most of the time? _____

   c. What tribe was supposed to conquer Ekron? _____

   d. Write down at least two facts about Ekron that you don't already know. _____

   _____

   _____

4. Based on your research, what kinds of remains would you expect to find in Ekron? _____

   _____

   _____

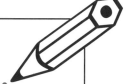

Written Artifacts and the Bible

1. To help you to understand that Abram's relationship with Sarai and Hagar was true to the social customs of the day revise the Nuzi adoption contract as follows:
   - Replace the name of Kelim-Nihu with Sarai.
   - Replace the name of Shennima with Abram.
   - Replace "a woman of the land of Lullu" with Hagar.

   The Tablet of Adoption belonging to Zike, the son of Akkuya: he gave his son Shennima in adoption to Shuriha-ilu, and Shuriha-ilu, with reference to Shennima, from all the land . . . and his earnings of every sort gave to Shennima one portion of his property. If Shuriha-ilu should have a son of his own, as the principal son he shall take a double share; Shennima shall then be next in order and take his proper share. As long as Shuriha-ilu is alive, Shennima shall revere him. When Shuriha-ilu dies, Shennima shall become heir.

   Furthermore, Kelim-ninu has been given in marriage to Shennima. If Kelim-ninu bears children, Shennima shall not take another wife; but if Kelim-ninu does not bear, Kelim-ninu shall acquire a woman of the land of Lullu as wife for Shennima, and Kelim-ninu may not send the offspring away. Any sons that may be born to Shennima from the womb of Kelim-ninu, to these sons shall be given all the lands and buildings of every sort.

   However, if she does not bear a son, then the daughter of Kelim-ninu from the lands and buildings shall take one portion of the property. Furthermore, Shuriha-ilu shall not adopt another son in addition to Shennima. Whoever among them defaults shall compensate with one mina of silver and one mina of gold.

2. Was it a custom for a wife to provide her husband with another wife if she was barren? _____
3. Was it a custom to send away the second wife and son if the first wife later had a son? _____
4. Was it a custom for the sons of the first wife to inherit all of the property? _____

5. Compare the following laws from Hammurabi's Code with God's laws.

   a. If a person's ox was in the habit of goring other animals or people and authorities had warned him, but he still did not control his ox, he paid the following fines: If the ox killed an upper class person the owner paid 8 oz. of silver. If the ox killed a slave the owner paid 5 oz. of silver. Compare this with Exodus 21:29–32. Write Moses' law in your own words.

   _____

   _____

   _____

   _____

   _____

   _____

   b. If a son struck his father, his hand was to be cut off. Compare this with Exodus 21:15. How is Moses' law the same or different? _____

   _____

   _____

   c. If a person stole the son of another person, he was to be put to death. Compare this with Exodus 21:16. How is Moses' law the same or different? _____

   _____

   _____

6. From these three examples, which laws seem to be harsher? Which seem fairer? Why?

   _____

   _____

   _____

   _____

   _____